SUPER SLEUTH

Gill SKILLS

3RD CLASS

Jacqueline Barry

g GILL EDUCATION

Gill Education
Hume Avenue
Park West
Dublin 12
www.gilleducation.ie

Gill Education is an imprint of M.H. Gill & Co.

© Jacqueline Barry 2017

ISBN: 978-0-7171-71835

Editor: Donna Garvin
Design and layout: Liz White Designs
Illustrations: Kate Shannon
Cover design: Slickfish
Cover illustration: Derry Dillon

The authors and publisher have made every effort to trace all copyright holders. If, however, any have been inadvertently overlooked, we would be pleased to make the necessary arrangement at the first opportunity.

The paper used in this book is made from the wood pulp of managed forests. For every tree felled, at least one tree is planted, thereby renewing natural resources.

Contents

How to Use this Book

Super Sleuth is a unique mathematical problem-solving series for 1st to 6th Class primary school pupils. Problem-solving requires pupils to understand and explore a problem, find a strategy, use the strategy to solve the problem and look back and reflect on the solution. *Super Sleuth* focuses on the process of problem-solving and the development of the **ten main problem-solving strategies**. The series has **regular built-in revision** units, which consolidate problem-solving skills.

Differentiation

Differentiation is catered for in each unit through the use of **bronze**, **silver** and **gold** medals that indicate the level of difficulty and provide an entry point for every pupil as well as opportunities for **high-achievers** to be challenged.

Collaborative learning

The series facilitates collaborative learning through **whole-class**, **pair** and **group work** activities. This creates an ideal classroom environment for pupils to develop their maths language and thinking, in which the teacher can act as facilitator and every pupil's contribution is valued. Learning can be applied at home through practice.

Dedicated strategy units

Each book dedicates **five units to a specific strategy** and pupils are encouraged to utilise and apply the strategies where relevant.

Super Sleuth's ten problem-solving strategies:

- Trial and improvement
- Working backwards
- Working systematically
- Logical reasoning
- Visualising/Draw a picture
- Identifying patterns
- Make a table
- Act it out
- Make a model
- Simplifying

Opportunity for
pair work

Duties

Reader
Calculator
Checker
Reporter

Opportunity for
group work

CLUES

CLUES is a teacher- and pupil-friendly **framework** developed uniquely for *Super Sleuth* to tackle the most common **problem-solving difficulties** experienced in the classroom. It was created in order to promote Bloom's higher forms of thinking in maths education.

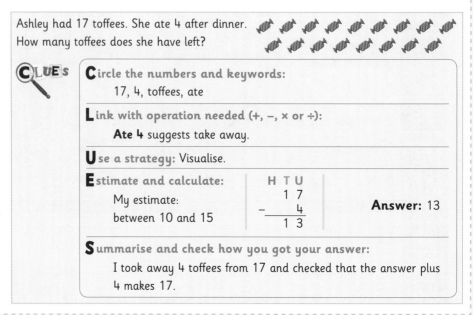

Ashley had 17 toffees. She ate 4 after dinner. How many toffees does she have left?

Circle the numbers and keywords:
   17, 4, toffees, ate

Link with operation needed (+, −, × or ÷):
   Ate 4 suggests take away.

Use a strategy: Visualise.

Estimate and calculate:

	H T U	
My estimate:	1 7	**Answer:** 13
between 10 and 15	− 4	
	1 3	

Summarise and check how you got your answer:
   I took away 4 toffees from 17 and checked that the answer plus 4 makes 17.

Super Sleuth key features

Weekly structure: Weekly arrangement of work (30 units) and provides four days of work with three to four questions per day.

WALT: Clear learning outcomes are provided at the beginning of each new strand.

Worked example: A worked example using the CLUES framework is provided at the start of new strands to demonstrate a strategy that pupils can follow, allowing them to work independently.

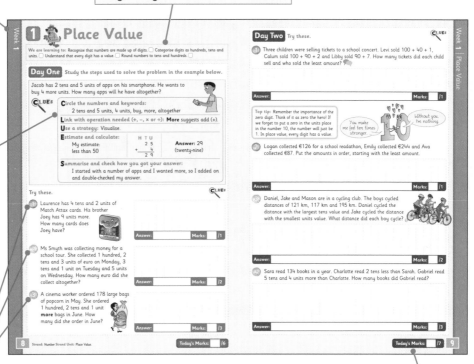

Clear differentiation: Each page is differentiated using bronze, silver and gold medals to show the level of difficulty and give pupils an incentive to progress. The bronze medal indicates a question that the majority of the class should work on independently. The silver medal poses more of a challenge, while the gold medal may require collaborative work in order for the pupils to reach a solution.

Progress recording: Each question and week has a score tracker to help pupils self-assess.

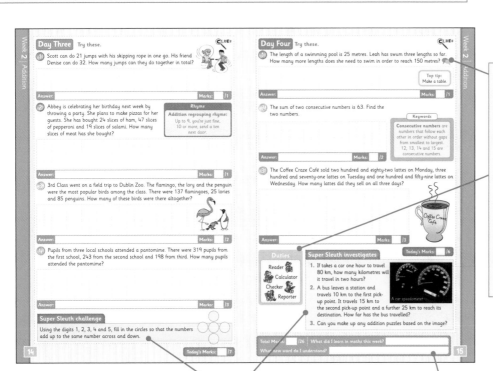

Pair work/group work: Opportunities are provided for pair and group work. Group work can be applied to activities and these specific questions are highlighted throughout the book, where different roles can be assigned to up to four pupils.

Puzzles and challenges: 'Super Sleuth challenge' is an open-ended question based on the maths skills and strand covered in the unit. 'Super Sleuth investigates' is an activity for applying the maths skills/strand of the unit to a situation that could be encountered in real life.

Self-assessment: The self-assessment section for each strand offers pupils an opportunity to reflect on their learning, as well as providing very valuable information to the teacher.

Problem-solving strategies

Trial and improvement

- The strategy of trial and improvement encourages pupils to make a reasonable estimate, giving them a starting point as they attempt to solve the puzzle.
- The pupils are then asked to check their estimate to see if it works as a solution and revise it accordingly.
- By repeating this process and changing their estimate appropriately, pupils should arrive at the correct answer.
- All rough work should be kept as a record of their work.

Example: On a farm there were some hens and cows. Altogether there were 8 heads and 22 feet. How many hens were there?

Working backwards

- Occasionally pupils come across a puzzle in which they are given the final answer and the steps taken to arrive at the answer, but they are not given the data from the start of the puzzle. They must undo each step to get back to the starting point.
- Pupils can draw a diagram to show the known facts and use the inverse operation when working backwards.

Example: Martha removed a loaf of bread from the oven after it had been baking for two hours. If she took it out at 4 o'clock, at what time did she put it into the oven?

Working systematically

- Working systematically requires pupils to work carefully through the information they are given.
- This strategy may incorporate other strategies for pupils to draw upon in order to work out the process of the problem. They might need to make a list, draw a diagram, make a table or explore problems with numerous answers in order to organise and build on the information until they find the solution.

Example: There are six ice-cream flavours to choose from. How many different two-scoop ice-cream cones can be made?

Logical reasoning

- Logical reasoning can be explained as a proper or reasonable way of thinking about something. It requires the pupils to think carefully about the information they have been given and decide on a way of using the information to solve the puzzle.
- Pupils are encouraged to use a step-by-step approach to reach a solution.
- This may involve implementing a strategy such as visualisation or making a table.

Example: Grumpy, Sneezy, Sleepy and Doc are all in line for the cinema. Sleepy is ahead of Grumpy, Sneezy is behind Grumpy and Doc is second. What is their order from first to last?

Visualising / Draw a picture

- Drawing a diagram can help pupils to visualise a puzzle. By doing this, they can make connections within the puzzle and plan how to solve it.
- Diagrams can include tree diagrams, timelines, pictures, symbols and Venn diagrams.

Example: Felix made 12 butterfly buns and iced them. He placed two chocolate buttons on top of each bun. How many chocolate buttons did he use?

Identifying patterns

- This strategy involves pupils investigating how numbers, images or symbols are arranged in a variety of orders.
- Each pattern follows a rule. Pupils may be asked to identify the rule in a pattern, find the missing value(s) or extend the existing pattern. Many things in our world follow a set of rules, so that we know what to expect.

Example: Millie is making a beaded necklace that follows a pattern of red, green, blue. If she uses 18 beads in total, how many red beads will she use?

Make a table

- When puzzles are written in word sentences, they can be confusing for pupils.
- Making a table helps pupils to organise the information that they have and identify the information that they need.

Example: Mikey saves €4 on Monday. Each day after that, he saves twice as much as the day before. How much money will he have saved by Friday?

Act it out

- Acting it out is an effective strategy for pupils who have difficulty visualising a problem.
- Acting out a problem using props such as cubes or string, or in pairs or groups can greatly simplify finding solutions and is an effective strategy for demonstration purposes in front of the whole class.

Example: I have a 5 litre jug and a 3 litre jug. How can I measure out 7 litres of juice using these jugs?

Make a model

- By making a model, the pupils are given an opportunity to showcase their understanding of a specific area of maths. For example, pupils can investigate the properties of 3-D shapes through model building.

Example: Using 26 cocktail sticks and Blu-tack, how many cubes can Emily make and how many cocktail sticks will be left over?

Simplifying

There are three ways in which pupils can simplify a puzzle:

- Reword the puzzle using a more familiar setting.
- Break the puzzle down into steps and solve one part at a time.
- Use smaller numbers.

Example: Amy spent $\frac{1}{8}$ of her savings on a new jacket. If she had €320 in savings, how much did the jacket cost?

$\frac{1}{8}$ of €32 = €4 ➡ $\frac{1}{8}$ of €320 = €40

1 Place Value

We are learning to: Recognise that numbers are made up of digits. ☐ Categorise digits as hundreds, tens and units. ☐ Understand that every digit has a value. ☐ Round numbers to tens and hundreds. ☐

Day One Study the steps used to solve the problem in the example below.

Jacob has 2 tens and 5 units of apps on his smartphone. He wants to buy 4 more units. How many apps will he have altogether?

CLUES

Circle the numbers and keywords:
2 tens and 5 units, 4 units, buy, more, altogether

Link with operation needed (+, −, × or ÷): **More** suggests add (+).

Use a strategy: Visualise.

Estimate and calculate:

	H	T	U
		2	5
+			4
		2	9

My estimate: less than 50

Answer: 29 (twenty-nine)

Summarise and check how you got your answer:
I started with a number of apps and I wanted more, so I added on and double-checked my answer.

Try these.

CLUES

1. Laurence has 4 tens and 2 units of Match Attax cards. His brother Joey has 9 units more. How many cards does Joey have?

Answer: _____ Marks: ___ /1

2. Ms Smyth was collecting money for a school tour. She collected 1 hundred, 2 tens and 3 units of euro on Monday, 3 tens and 1 unit on Tuesday and 5 units on Wednesday. How many euro did she collect altogether?

Answer: _____ Marks: ___ /2

3. A cinema worker ordered 178 large bags of popcorn in May. She ordered 1 hundred, 2 tens and 1 unit **more** bags in June. How many did she order in June?

Answer: _____ Marks: ___ /3

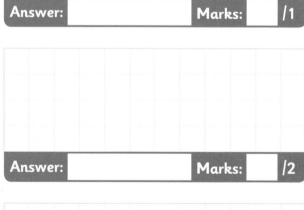

Strand: Number Strand Unit: Place Value

Today's Marks: ___ /6

Day Two Try these.

① Three children were selling tickets to a school concert. Levi sold 100 + 40 + 1, Calum sold 100 + 90 + 2 and Libby sold 90 + 7. How many tickets did each child sell and who sold the least amount?

Answer: | **Marks:** | /1

Top tip: Remember the importance of the zero digit. Think of it as zero the hero! If we forget to put a zero in the units place in the number 10, the number will just be 1. In place value, every digit has a value.

You make me feel ten times stronger.

Without you, I'm nothing.

② Logan collected €126 for a school readathon, Emily collected €244 and Ava collected €87. Put the amounts in order, starting with the least amount.

Answer: | **Marks:** | /1

③ Daniel, Jake and Mason are in a cycling club. The boys cycled distances of 121 km, 117 km and 195 km. Daniel cycled the distance with the largest tens value and Jake cycled the distance with the smallest units value. What distance did each boy cycle?

Answer: | **Marks:** | /2

④ Sara read 134 books in a year. Charlotte read 2 tens less than Sarah. Gabriel read 5 tens and 4 units more than Charlotte. How many books did Gabriel read?

Answer: | **Marks:** | /3

Today's Marks: | /7

Day Three Try these.

1 There were 219 Twistables in the teacher's drawer. She buys 124 more and adds them to the drawer. By rounding your answer to the nearest ten, how many Twistables are in the drawer now?

Answer: **Marks:** /1

2 In January, Joe the gardener planted 327 bulbs in the local park. He planted 63 bulbs in February and 45 bulbs in March. By rounding your answer to the nearest ten, how many bulbs did he plant altogether?

Answer: **Marks:** /1

3 At a birthday party, there were 127 party poppers. 14 were popped before the cake was cut and 36 were popped afterwards. How many party poppers were left to pop? Round your answer to the nearest ten.

Answer: **Marks:** /2

4 A sports shop sold 457 jerseys in September, 345 jerseys in October and 142 jerseys in November. How many jerseys were sold in total? Round your answer to the nearest hundred.

Answer: **Marks:** /3

Super Sleuth challenge

What is the greatest three-digit number you can make with digits that total 14?

A **digit** (numeral) is a symbol used to make numbers. 0, 1, 2, 3, 4, 5, 6, 7, 8, 9 are the ten digits that we use to make numbers. The value of each digit depends on its place in a number.

Today's Marks: /7

Day Four Try these.

 I am a three-digit number. If you add up my digits, they total 10. If my tens digit is 7, what are my other two digits? (There is more than one answer.)

Answer: _____ Marks: [ ] /1

 Michaela typed a three-digit number on her iPad. She gave her friends the following clues about the number. Can you work out the number?

- The hundreds place value and the units place value have the same digit.
- The tens place value is one less than the hundreds place value.
- The units place value is the highest digit.

Answer: _____ Marks: [ ] /2

Alex wrote down a three-digit number and asked the class to guess what it was. He gave them the following hints. Can you work out the number?

- The hundreds digit is 8 greater than the units digit.
- The tens digit is 4 greater than the units digit.
- The sum of all three digits is 15.

Top tip: Use trial and improvement.

Answer: _____ Marks: [ ] /3

Puzzle power

Today's Marks: [ ] /6

| 9 | 0 | 4 | 1 | 2 | 7 |

In your copy, using only the digits above:

1. Make a three-digit number greater than 455.
2. Make a three-digit number with a tens digit that is double the units digit.
3. Make the biggest three-digit number possible.
4. Make the smallest three-digit number possible.
5. Make the biggest three-digit number possible with 4 in the tens place.
6. Make up a question for your partner and get them to guess the number.

Total Marks: [ ] /26 | What strategy did I learn this week? _____

I got confused about _____

11

2 Addition

We are learning to: Add up numbers under the correct place value. ☐ Recall addition facts. ☐
Regroup 10 units to make a ten and 10 tens to make a hundred. ☐

Day One — Study the steps used to solve the problem in the example below.

There are 36 bicycles in Cool Cycles shop. The owner buys 23 more. How many bicycles are there altogether now?

CLUES

Circle the numbers and keywords:
> 36, 23, bicycles, buys, more, altogether

Link with operation needed (+, −, × or ÷):
> **More** means add (+). **Altogether** also means add.

Use a strategy: Visualise.

Estimate and calculate:

My estimate: around 50

```
  H T U
    3 6
+   2 3
    5 9
```

Answer: 59
(fifty-nine)

Summarise and check how you got your answer:
> I lined up <u>the units below the units</u> and <u>the tens below the tens.</u>
> I double-checked my answer.

Try these.

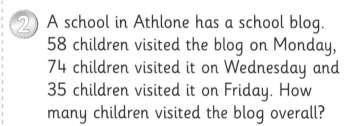

CLUES

1 Rosie loves making loom-band bracelets. She needs 43 bands to make one. How many does she need to make two?

Answer: _____ Marks: ___ /1

2 A school in Athlone has a school blog. 58 children visited the blog on Monday, 74 children visited it on Wednesday and 35 children visited it on Friday. How many children visited the blog overall?

Answer: _____ Marks: ___ /2

3 A postman delivers the post to four estates. Every day, he delivers to 37 houses in the first estate, 126 houses in the second estate and 84 houses each in the third and fourth estates. How many houses does he have to visit?

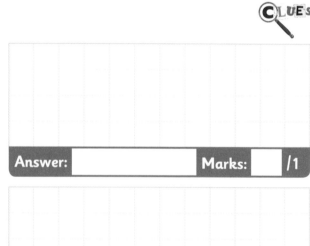

Answer: _____ Marks: ___ /3

Strand: Number Strand Unit: Operations – addition

Today's Marks: ___ /6

Day Two Try these.

1 At a newsagent, the most popular magazine sold 165 copies on Saturday and 243 copies on Sunday. How many copies were sold altogether?

Answer: | Marks: | /1

2 Aer Lingus flies from Dublin to London and back daily. If the distance each way is 464 km, what distance does an aeroplane travel on a return trip?

Answer: | Marks: | /1

3 A coach ordered training jerseys for her football club. She ordered 216 small, 136 medium and 204 large jerseys. How many jerseys did she order?

Maths words

Vocabulary of addition: add, more, plus, increase, sum, total, altogether, score, double, near double, how many more?

Answer: | Marks: | /2

4 After school, Leon played Minecraft online. Including Leon, 314 players were online in the first minute of the game. In the second minute, 142 more players joined and in the third minute, an additional 268 players joined. How many players were there in the third minute?

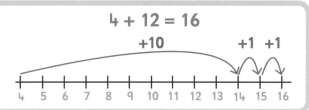

Top tip:
Remember the jump strategy when adding mentally (in your head). We can count in 2s or 10s or make any jumps that we want in order to do a calculation.

4 + 12 = 16

+10   +1 +1

4 5 6 7 8 9 10 11 12 13 14 15 16

Answer: | Marks: | /3

Today's Marks: | /7

13

Day Three Try these.

CLUEs

1. Scott can do 21 jumps with his skipping rope in one go. His friend Denise can do 32. How many jumps can they do together in total?

Answer: **Marks:** /1

2. Abbey is celebrating her birthday next week by throwing a party. She plans to make pizzas for her guests. She has bought 24 slices of ham, 47 slices of pepperoni and 19 slices of salami. How many slices of meat has she bought?

Rhyme

Addition regrouping rhyme:
Up to 9, you're just fine,
10 or more, send a ten next door.

Answer: **Marks:** /1

3. 3rd Class went on a field trip to Dublin Zoo. The flamingo, the lory and the penguin were the most popular birds among the class. There were 137 flamingoes, 25 lories and 85 penguins. How many of these birds were there altogether?

Answer: **Marks:** /2

4. Pupils from three local schools attended a pantomime. There were 319 pupils from the first school, 243 from the second school and 198 from the third school. How many pupils attended the pantomime?

Answer: **Marks:** /3

Super Sleuth challenge

Using the digits 1, 2, 3, 4 and 5, fill in the circles so that the numbers add up to the same number across and down.

Today's Marks: /7

Day Four Try these.

1 The length of a swimming pool is 25 metres. Leah has swum three lengths so far. How many more lengths does she need to swim in order to reach 150 metres?

Top tip:
Make a table.

Answer: _____ Marks: ___ /1

2 The sum of two consecutive numbers is 63. Find the two numbers.

Keywords

Consecutive numbers are numbers that follow each other in order without gaps from smallest to largest. 12, 13, 14 and 15 are consecutive numbers.

Answer: _____ Marks: ___ /2

3 The Coffee Craze Café sold two hundred and eighty-two lattes on Monday, three hundred and seventy-one lattes on Tuesday and one hundred and fifty-nine lattes on Wednesday. How many lattes did they sell on all three days?

Answer: _____ Marks: ___ /3

Today's Marks: ___ /6

Duties

Reader
Calculator
Checker
Reporter

Super Sleuth investigates

1. If it takes a car one hour to travel 80 km, how many kilometres will it travel in two hours?

2. A bus leaves a station and travels 10 km to the first pick-up point. It travels 15 km to the second pick-up point and a further 25 km to reach its destination. How far has the bus travelled?

A car speedometer

3. Can you make up any addition puzzles based on the image?

Total Marks: ___ /26 | What did I learn in maths this week? _____

What new word do I understand? _____

3  Lines and Angles

We are learning to: Identify parallel lines. ☐ Describe an angle greater than, less than or equal to a right angle. ☐ Classify horizontal and vertical lines. ☐

Day One Study the steps used to solve the problem in the example below.

What types of line do railway tracks make?

Keywords

Parallel lines are always the same distance apart, never touch and point in the same direction.

Circle the numbers and keywords: types of line, railway tracks

Link with operation needed (+, −, × or ÷): None

Use a strategy: Visualise.

Estimate and calculate:
My estimate: straight lines

Lines that run side by side and never meet are called parallel lines.

Answer: parallel lines

Summarise and check how you got your answer:
I double-checked my answer.

Try these.

Top tip: Visualise.

1. Look at the image. What type of line does the tightrope make?

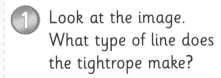

Answer: _____
Marks: ___ /1

2. Look at the image. What types of line do the strings on the harp make?

Answers: _____
and _____
Marks: ___ /2

3. Look at the capital letters below. Which ones have vertical lines? Which ones have horizontal lines?

Vertical: _____
Horizontal _____
Marks: ___ /3

I N H K P L R E F Z

Today's Marks: ___ /6

Day Two Try these.

1. A figure skater can spin in two directions. What are they? 💬

Maths words

Vocabulary of lines and angles:
vertical line, horizontal line, parallel lines, right angle, greater than a right angle, less than a right angle, clockwise direction, anti-clockwise direction

Answers:

or

Marks: /1

2. A group in class were playing a game of Twister during golden time. Lara spun the spinner. What type of angle did the spinner make?

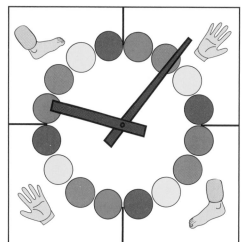

Answer:

Marks: /1

3. Jasmine ordered a large pizza to share with her friends. The pizza was cut into 12 slices. What type of angle did each slice make?

Answer:

Marks: /2

4. Name the types of line and the type of angle found in the American flag.

Lines:

and

Angle:

Marks: /3

Rhyme

Horizontal lines go left to right, side to side, side to side. Vertical lines are standing tall, up and down, up and down.

Joke!

Parallel lines have so much in common. It's a shame they will never meet!

Today's Marks: /7

17

Day Three Try these.

CLUES

1. Look at the plan of Sarah's bedroom. At what angle is her desk positioned?

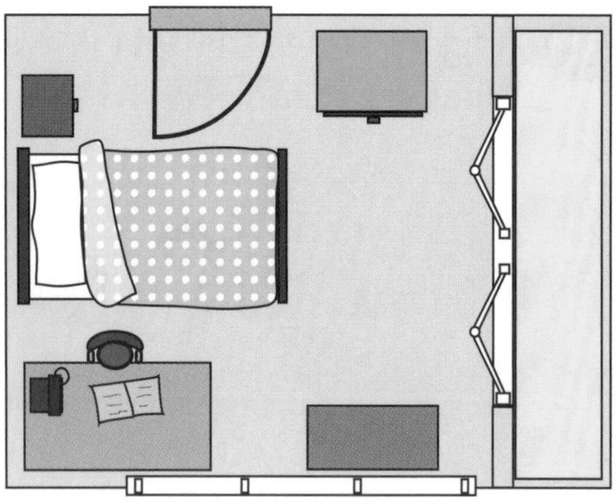

Joke!
Never argue with a 90° angle. It's always right!

Answer:
Marks: /1

2. Josh's dad is painting the house. What angle does the ladder make against the wall?

Answer:
Marks: /1

3. Greg's bicycle wheel has been damaged in an accident. Less than half of the spokes have broken off. What type of angle do the remaining spokes make?

Answer:
Marks: /2

4. A swimmer dives into the deep end of the pool. What angle do her arms make with the water?

Answer:
Marks: /3

Super Sleuth challenge

What if buildings were designed without angles? What would they look like? Draw your design.

Today's Marks: /7

Day Four Try these.

Megan, Dillon and Jeremy walk home from school in different directions. This is a map of their neighbourhood. 💬

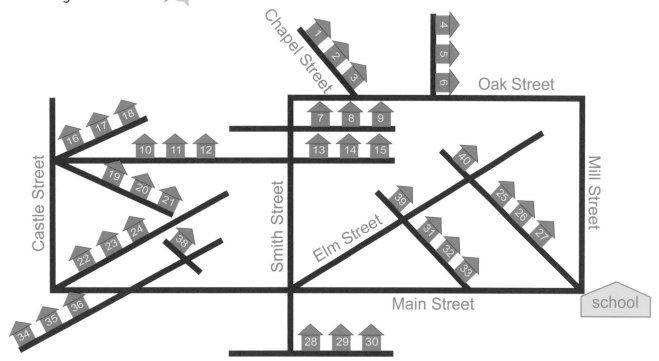

1. Megan's journey: Take the horizontal road from the school. At the crossroads, turn onto the first diagonal road that forms an angle less than a right angle with Main Street. Continue onto the second parallel road, turn right and go to the second house. What is Megan's house number?

Answer: _____ Marks: ___ /1

2. Dillon's journey: Take the vertical road from the school. At the end of the road, turn left. Pass the road that makes a right angle with the one you are on. Turn right onto the road that makes an angle greater than a right angle with the one you are on. Dillion's house is the third on the right. What is its number?

Answer: _____ Marks: ___ /2

3. Jeremy's journey: Take the horizontal road from the school. Go straight through the first and second crossroads. When you come to a junction that makes a right angle with the road you are on, turn right and continue until you come the next junction. Turn right onto the road that makes a right angle with the one you are on and go to the third house. What is Jeremy's house number?

Answer: _____ Marks: ___ /3

Today's Marks: ___ /6

Total Marks: ___ /26 | When I get stuck on a question, I _____

I could now teach a friend how to _____

19

4 Time

We are learning to: Read time in five-minute intervals. ☐ Read and interpret simple timetables. ☐
Record time in analogue and digital forms. ☐ Rename minutes as hours and hours as minutes. ☐

Day One Study the steps used to solve the problem in the example below.

I arrive home from school at 3:30 pm. I go to bed 5 hours later. At what time do I go to bed?

CLUES

Top tip: Count on when adding time.

Circle the numbers and keywords:
  3:30, 5 hours, school, bed, later, time

Link with operation needed (+, −, × or ÷):
  5 hours **later** means count on.

Use a strategy: Act it out.

Estimate and calculate:
| My estimate: 8:00 pm | Count on. 3 + 5 = 8 | **Answer:** 8:30 pm (half past 8) |

Summarise and check how you got your answer:
  I double-checked my answer.

Try these.

CLUES

1. Maisie begins ballet practice every Tuesday at 20 past 6. Practice lasts for 40 minutes. At what time does it finish?

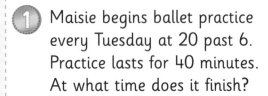

$$20 + 40 = 60$$
$$2 + 4 = 6$$

Answer: 7:00   Marks: ☐ /1

2. The FA Cup Final will kick off at 2 o'clock on Saturday. The match should last 90 minutes with a 15-minute break at half-time. At what time should the match finish?

Answer: 3:45   Marks: ☐ /2

3. The Cub Scouts went hillwalking on Sunday. They walked from a quarter to 9 until 11 o'clock. They took a break for half an hour and then walked back to base. If they arrived back at base at 2 o'clock, how long did they spend walking?

Answer: 4hrs 45mins   Marks: ☐ /3

Strand: Measures Strand Unit: Time

Today's Marks: ☐ /6

Day Two Try these.

1 Zoe and Hannah went to a concert that began at 6 o'clock and lasted 2 hours and 15 minutes. At what time did the concert end?

Top tip:

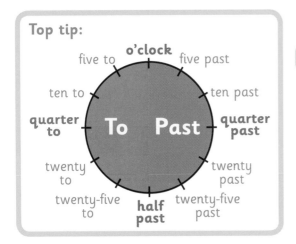

five to   o'clock   five past

ten to   ten past

quarter to   **To**   **Past**   quarter past

twenty to   twenty past

twenty-five to   half past   twenty-five past

Top tip: Act it out.

Answer: 8:15   **Marks:** /1

2 Samuel got on the Ferris wheel at an amusement park at 3:15 pm. If the ride lasted 20 minutes, at what time did Samuel get off?

$$15 + 20 = 35$$

Answer: 3:35   **Marks:** /1

Top tip: Being able to skip count in 5s makes reading an analogue clock and learning to add time much easier.

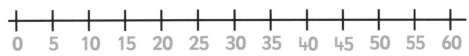

0   5   10   15   20   25   30   35   40   45   50   55   60

3 Goodreads Bookshop held a book launch on Saturday morning at 10:30 am. The author signed copies of her new book for 45 minutes. At what time did she finish?

$$30 + 45$$

Answer: 11:15   **Marks:** /2

4 The new *Star Wars* film starts at 5:20 pm sharp in Omniplex. If the film is 2 hours and 10 minutes long, at what time will it end?

$$20 + 130$$

Answer: 7:30   **Marks:** /3

Today's Marks: /7   21

Day Three Try these.

1 Jaxon's birthday is on Saturday, October 14th. The venue he plans to hire for his party has already been booked on this date, so he will hire it one week later instead. On what date will his party be held?

Sunday	Monday	Tuesday	Wednesday	Thursday	Friday	Saturday
			OCTOBER			
1	2	3	4	5	6	7
8	9	10	11	12	13	14
15	16	17	18	19	20	21
22	23	24	25	26	27	28
29	30	31				

Answer: _____ **Marks:** ___ /1

2 A school chess competition was due to take place on Wednesday, November 8th, but it got postponed for two weeks. On what date will the competition take place now?

Answer: _____ **Marks:** ___ /1

3 Mrs Silverwood had a dentist's appointment 10 days ago. If today is Friday, September 1st, on what date was her appointment?

Answer: _____ **Marks:** ___ /2

4 In a leap year, I order a new television on Thursday, February 22nd. The seller tells me that it will take 14 days for the television to be delivered. On what date should I expect it to arrive?

Answer: _____ **Marks:** ___ /3

Super Sleuth challenge

1. When does time not matter?

2. Can you think of a situation in which you would not need to know the time?

Rhyme

30 days have September, April, June and November. All the rest have 31, except for February alone, which has 28 days clear and 29 in each leap year.

Today's Marks: ___ /7

Day Four Try these.

Cork Airport Departures		
Destination	Flight No.	Departs
Alicante	EI856	6:20 am
London City	FR902	6:25 am
Malaga	FR9901	6:30 am
Birmingham	EI3700	6:45 am
Manchester	EI3720	7:00 am
Edinburgh	EI3806	7:00 am
Manchester	EY7943	7:00 am
London Heathrow	BA5910	7:20 am

Cork Airport Arrivals		
Origin	Flight No.	Arrives
Jersey	EI3924	10:10 am
Bristol	EI3842	10:35 am
Faro	EI896	11:30 am
London Heathrow	BA5912	11:40 am
London Heathrow	EI712	12:05 pm
London City	WX314	12:15 pm
Paris CDG	EI822	12:30 pm
Düsseldorf	EI830	1:15 pm

1. Flight EY7943 from Cork to Manchester took 1 hour and 35 minutes. At what time did it land in Manchester?

7:00 + 1hr = 8:00 + 35 mins = 8:35

Answer: 8:35   Marks: /1

2. Flight EI822 left Paris at 10:50 am. How long is the flight expected to take?

10:50 to 12:30

Answer: 1hr 40mins   Marks: /2

3. The journey time from London to Cork is about 1 hour and 20 minutes. What is the latest flight that I could take from London if I needed to be in Cork by 2:00 pm?

Answer: 12:30   Marks: /3

Today's Marks: /6

Duties

Reader
Calculator
Checker
Reporter

Super Sleuth investigates

1. Look at the image. Emily has gymnastics practice at 1 o'clock. How many minutes until it starts?

2. Gymnastics practice lasts for 45 minutes. At what time will it end?

3. How much time do you think the gymnasts might spend warming up?

Total Marks: /26 | In this unit, I liked Day Four and time for flights

I understand more about flight time tables

23

5  Revision 1

The Olympic Games

The Summer Olympic Games and the Winter Olympic Games both take place every four years, but they are held two years apart. The Olympic rings represent five regions of the world: Europe, Africa, the Americas, Asia and Oceania.

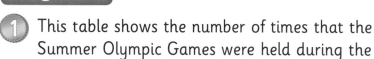 **Day One** Try these.

Region	No. of times
Europe	1 ten and 7 units
North America	6 units
Asia	2 units
Oceania	1 unit
Total:	

1 This table shows the number of times that the Summer Olympic Games were held during the twentieth century. How many times in total were the Summer Olympic Games held during this period?

Answer: _____ Marks: ___ /1

2 8 tens and 2 units of countries take part in the Winter Olympic Games. 1 hundred, 2 tens and 3 units of countries take part in the Summer Olympic Games. How many countries in total participate in the Olympic Games?

Answer: _____ Marks: ___ /1

3 The USA team topped the medal tally in the 2016 Summer Olympic Games, winning 40 + 4 gold, 30 + 7 silver and 30 + 8 bronze. How many medals did they bring back to their country?

Answer: _____ Marks: ___ /2

4 At the 2016 Summer Olympic Games, there were seventy-seven athletes from Ireland, three hundred and seventy-three from Great Britain and five hundred and fifty-eight from the USA. How many more athletes were there from the USA than from Ireland and Great Britain combined?

Answer: _____ Marks: ___ /3

Strand: Number Strand Units: Place Value; Operations – addition
Strand: Shape and Space Strand Unit: Lines and Angles Strand: Measures Strand Unit: Time

Today's Marks: ___ /7

Day Two Try these.

Top tip: Make a table.

1 It takes the Olympic athletes 40 minutes to travel from the Olympic Village to Arena 5 by bus. If the bus leaves at 9:10 am, at what time will they arrive?

Answer: _____ Marks: ___ /1

2 The Summer Olympic Games run for 17 days. If they start on August 5th, on what date are they due to finish?

Answer: _____ Marks: ___ /1

3 An Olympic runner can run around a 400 m track in 50 seconds. How long will it take him to run around it three times?

Answer: _____ Marks: ___ /2

4 Two of the outdoor tennis events were postponed by 20 minutes due to rain, as they needed to cover the court. Calculate the new starting times for these events.

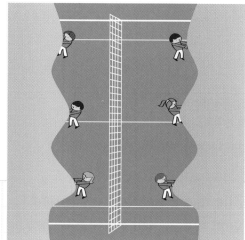

Event	Original Time	New Time
(a) Men's Singles	11:05 am	?
(b) Women's Singles	7:50 pm	?

Answers: (a) _____ (b) _____ Marks: ___ /3

Today's Marks: ___ /7

Day Three Try these.

1 Each competitor has 3 attempts at the javelin throw. What type of angle does the javelin make with the ground?

Answer: _____ Marks: ☐ /1

2 (a) What types of line can you find in the high jump stand?

(b) How many lines would there be in 10 similar stands?

Answers: (a) _____ (b) _____ Marks: ☐ /1

3 (a) How many right angles do you see on this tennis court?

(b) How many would there be on 2 tennis courts?

Answers: (a) _____ (b) _____ Marks: ☐ /2

4 There are 10 lanes in an Olympic swimming pool, which are created using ropes.

(a) What type of lines do the ropes make?

(b) How many ropes are needed to make 10 lanes?
(Hint: A rope is not needed at the sides of the pool.)

Top tip: Visualise or act it out.

Answers: (a) _____ (b) _____ Marks: ☐ /3

Puzzle power

The five Olympic rings create nine areas, which are labelled A to I in the image. Using the digits 1, 2, 3, 4, 5, 6, 7, 8 and 9, number each area so that the digits in every ring add up to the same number.

A   C   E
B   G   D   I
F   H

Today's Marks: ☐ /7

Day Four Try these.

1. 5 athletes took part in the gymnastics heats. Each athlete's routine lasted 3 minutes and there were 4 one-minute breaks between the routines. For how many minutes did the gymnastics heats last in total?

Top tip: Identify a pattern.

CLUE's

Answer: _____ Marks: ☐ /1

2. In the soccer league, there are 16 men's teams and 12 women's teams. Each team has 3 subsitute players. How many subsitute players are there in total?

Answer: _____ Marks: ☐ /2

3. In 2012, London hosted the Summer Olympic Games. If 600 balls, 53 helmets and 120 ropes were used, how many pieces of equipment was this in total?

Answer: _____ Marks: ☐ /3

Today's Marks: ☐ /6

Duties

Reader
Calculator
Checker
Reporter

Super Sleuth investigates

1. What shapes can you identify in this image?

2. The poles create parallel lines. Can you find any other types of line?

3. Can you think of any maths questions based on the image?

Total Marks: ☐ /27

6  Strategy: Trial and Improvement

Day One

The strategy of trial and improvement encourages you to think about a number story carefully. This helps you to make intelligent estimates (guesses) about the answer and then break down your estimates until you arrive at the correct answer. Use the rough work area to keep trying and double-checking your calculations until you arrive at the correct answer.

> The sum of two numbers is 11 and they have a difference of 1. What are the two numbers?

Try these.

CLUES

1. There are 2 pet cats in the Darcy household, Fluffy and Cotton. Fluffy is 2 years older than Cotton. If their combined age is 16, how old is each cat? Estimate first!

Answer: _____ Marks: ___ /1

2. Natalie is 4 years older than Nora, who is 2 years older than Lucy. Together their ages add up to 20. How old are the girls? Estimate first!

Answer: _____ Marks: ___ /1

3. In a class of 33 pupils, there are 3 more boys than girls. How many boys and how many girls are there in the class? Estimate first!

Answer: _____ Marks: ___ /2

4. There are 56 girls in the under-10s hockey division. They are spilt into three groups: group A, group B and group C. If group A has 4 more girls than the other groups, how many girls are there in each group?

Answer: _____ Marks: ___ /3

Today's Marks: ___ /7

Day Two Try these.

Use the strategy of trial and improvement to solve each number story below.

1 The sum of two numbers is 11 and their product is 30. What are the two numbers?

Answer: **Marks:**   /1

Remember: The **sum** is the result of adding two or more numbers, e.g. 9 is the sum of 2, 4 and 3. The **product** is the result of multiplying two or more numbers together, e.g. the product of 4 and 7 is 28.

2 I am thinking of a two-digit number. The tens value is greater than the units value. The sum of the digits is 12 and their product is 35. What is the number?

Answer: **Marks:**   /1

3 When three consecutive numbers are added, they total 63. What are the three numbers?

?+?+?=63

Answer: **Marks:**   /2

4 The product of two numbers is 126. One of the numbers is 5 more than the other. Can you find the two numbers?

Answer: **Marks:**   /3

Super Sleuth challenge

Can you think of your own questions involving sum and product to test your partner?

Today's Marks: /7   **29**

Day Three Try these.

Use the strategy of trial and improvement to solve each number story below.

1. Emily, Rachel and Katie competed in the long jump at sports day. They jumped lengths of 133 cm, 176 cm and 150 cm. Rachel jumped the farthest and Katie jumped an odd number of centimetres. What length did each girl jump?

Answer: | **Marks:** | /1

2. There are 6 more boxes of red apples than green apples at a supermarket. In all, there are 16 boxes of apples. How many boxes of green apples are there?

Answer: | **Marks:** | /1

3. Liam bought a box of chocolates and a box of mints. There were 14 fewer mints than chocolates and there were 28 chocolates. How many treats were there in total?

Answer: | **Marks:** | /2

4. Victoria gave her mum a bouquet of 24 flowers. It was made up of lilies, daffodils and irises. There were twice as many lilies as irises and three times as many daffodils as irises. How many of each flower was there?

Answer: | **Marks:** | /3

Today's Marks: | /7

Day Four Try these.

Use the strategy of trial and improvement to solve each number story below.

1 A restaurant sold 4 more bowls of tomato soup than vegetable soup. They sold 18 bowls of soup in total. How many bowls of tomato soup did they sell?

Answer: _____ Marks: ___ /1

2 At a tag rugby match between the Scrum Crushers and the Kicktators, there were 14 fans watching from the sidelines. The Scrum Crushers had 6 more fans than the Kicktators. How many fans did the Scrum Crushers have?

Go Scrum Crushers

Answer: _____ Marks: ___ /2

3 Robin and Richard receive €15 pocket money between them every week. Robin does more chores around the house, so he gets €3 more than Richard. How much pocket money do they each receive?

Answer: _____ Marks: ___ /3

Today's Marks: ___ /6

Total Marks: ___ /27 | I found this difficult: _____

I liked working in pairs, because _____

7  Subtraction

We are learning to: Subtract, without and with renaming, within 999. ☐ Know and recall subtraction facts. ☐

Day One Study the steps used to solve the problem in the example below.

Ashley had 17 toffees. She ate 4 after dinner. How many toffees does she have left?

Circle the numbers and keywords:
17, 4, toffees, ate

Link with operation needed (+, −, × or ÷):
Ate 4 suggests take away.

Use a strategy: Visualise.

Estimate and calculate:

My estimate:
between 10 and 15

H	T	U
	1	7
−		4
	1	3

Answer: 13

Summarise and check how you got your answer:
I took away 4 toffees from 17 and checked that the answer plus 4 makes 17.

Try these.

1. Eleanor has 56 music albums on her smartphone. She needs storage, so she deletes 24 of them. How many albums are left?

Answer: _____ Marks: ___ /1

2. There are 28 girls in 3rd Class. 19 of them attend tennis practice every Wednesday. How many girls do not attend tennis practice?

Answer: _____ Marks: ___ /2

3. There are 60 jellies in a packet. 23 of them are red, 31 are blue and the rest are green. How many green jellies are there?

Answer: _____ Marks: ___ /3

Today's Marks: ___ /6

Day Two Try these.

CLUEs

1 The local film-rental shop has a wide selection of DVDs and Blu-rays available. Altogether there are 876. If there are 324 DVDs, how many Blu-rays are there?

Answer: | **Marks:** | /1

2 Jacob needs 690 points to complete level one on his PlayStation game. He already has 478 points. How many more points does he need to get to level two?

Answer: | **Marks:** | /1

3 GAA Cúl Camps take place annually during the summer months. There were 502 children present at one location this year. 369 were boys. How many girls were there?

Answer: | **Marks:** | /2

Top tip: If you want to subtract without regrouping, take 1 away from the top number and the bottom number before you start. This makes it easier to subtract.

$$
\begin{array}{r} 7\ 0\ 0 \\ -\ 1\ 3\ 4 \end{array} \longrightarrow \begin{array}{r} 6\ 9\ 9 \\ -\ 1\ 3\ 3 \end{array}
$$

4 Rico, Stacey and Philip collect soccer cards. With 127 cards, Stacey has the most. Rico has 45 less than Stacey and Philip has 17 more than Rico. How many cards does Philip have?

Maths words

Vocabulary of subtraction: take away, subtract, less, decrease, difference, minus, spend, remove, how many less?

Answer: | **Marks:** | /3

Day Three Try these.

1. Layla's mum paid €68 for a school tracksuit, €55 for a pair of runners and €37 for a new gym bag. How much change did she get from €200?

Top tip: Work backwards.

Answer: ____ Marks: __ /1

2. 360 people attended a concert. There were 125 people sitting upstairs and 47 people sitting on the balcony. The rest were sitting downstairs. How many were sitting downstairs?

Rhyme

Remember when renaming:

More on top, no need to stop.

More on the floor, go next door and get 10 more!

$$257$$
$$- 39$$

Hey, man, if you could spare a ten, it would really help me out.

Answer: ____ Marks: __ /1

3. Victoria had 654 songs on her MP3 player, but she deleted half of them by accident. Of the deleted songs, 143 were rock music and the rest were pop music. How many of the deleted songs were pop music?

Answer: ____ Marks: __ /2

4. On Thursday, a butcher sold 120 kg of beef. On Friday, he sold twice that amount. On Saturday, he sold 180 kg of beef. How much more beef did he sell on Friday than on Saturday?

Answer: ____ Marks: __ /3

Today's Marks: ____ /7

Day Four Try these.

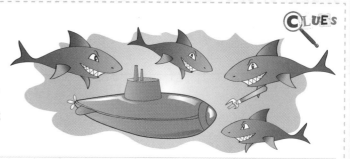

1. A submarine was positioned 300 m below sea level. It rose 74 m one hour and 25 m the next hour. What was its new position?

Answer: _____ **Marks:** ___ /1

2. A playground fence measuring 250 m needed a fresh coat of paint. The painters completed 87 m on Monday and a further 62 m on Tuesday. What length of the fence had they left to paint?

Answer: _____ **Marks:** ___ /2

3. Castle United Football Club has €892 to spend on new gear. They need new jerseys costing €326, new shorts costing €257 and new footballs costing €145. How much money will be left over?

Answer: _____ **Marks:** ___ /3

Today's Marks: ___ /6

Duties

Reader

Calculator

Checker

Reporter

Super Sleuth investigates

A bakery sells 30 different types of cake.

A delivery arrives every morning containing 10 of each type of cake. One day, half of the delivery was sold and the owner took home 20 cakes. How many cakes were left over?

In your copy, can you write your own question based on the image?

Total Marks: ___ /26 **I feel more confident about** _____

My favourite question was _____

8  Data

We are learning to: Collect, organise and represent data using pictograms, block graphs and bar charts. ☐
Read and understand tables, pictograms, block graphs and bar charts. ☐

Day One Study the steps used to solve the problem in the example below.

How many ice-cream cones in total were sold at this ice-cream parlour?

Chocolate	🍦🍦🍦		Strawberry	🍦🍦🍦🍦🍦
Vanilla	🍦🍦🍦🍦🍦🍦🍦🍦🍦🍦		Banana	🍦🍦
Mint	🍦🍦🍦🍦🍦🍦🍦🍦			

 Circle the numbers and keywords:
   3, 10, 8, 5, 2, ice-cream cones, sold

Link with operation needed (+, −, × or ÷): **Total** means add (+).

Use a strategy: Visualise.

Estimate and calculate:

My estimate:
5 groups of 5 = 25

| 3 + 10 + 8 + 5 + 2 = 28 | **Answer:** 28 |

Summarise and check how you got your answer:
   I double-checked my answer by counting on.

Try these.

1. Based on the pictogram above, what is the difference between the most popular and the least popular flavours of ice-cream?

Answer: _____ Marks: ___ /1

2. **(a)** Which flavour sold more than banana, but less than strawberry?
(b) Which two flavours have a combined total of 13? (There is more than one answer.)

Answer: (a) _____
(b) _____ Marks: ___ /2

3. If 24 more ice-cream cones were sold that evening, how many were sold in total?

Answer: _____ Marks: ___ /3

Today's Marks: ___ /6

Day Two Try these.

Top tip: Act it out.

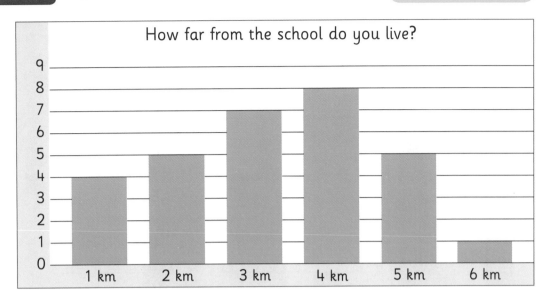

How far from the school do you live?

1. How many children in the group live **less than** 4 km from the school?

Answer: | Marks: | /1

2. On Wednesday, the children try to walk to school. Those living 5 km or more from the school are allowed to be late. How many children is that?

Answer: | Marks: | /1

3. How many more children live 4 km or less from the school than children who live 5 km or more from the school?

Answer: | Marks: | /2

4. How many children in total were asked how far they lived from their school?

Answer: | Marks: | /3

Today's Marks: | /7

Day Three Try these.

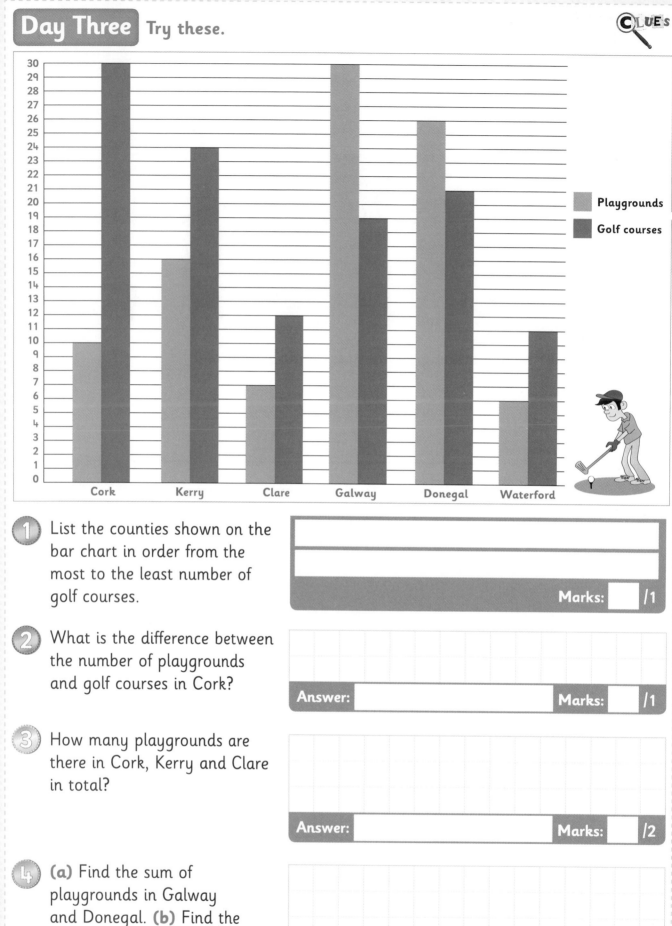

1. List the counties shown on the bar chart in order from the most to the least number of golf courses.

Marks: /1

2. What is the difference between the number of playgrounds and golf courses in Cork?

Answer: Marks: /1

3. How many playgrounds are there in Cork, Kerry and Clare in total?

Answer: Marks: /2

4. **(a)** Find the sum of playgrounds in Galway and Donegal. **(b)** Find the **difference** between the sum of playgrounds and golf courses in Galway and Donegal.

Answer: (a)   (b)   Marks: /3

Today's Marks: /7

Day Four Try these.

1 The owner of a Chinese restaurant recorded the dishes ordered on Saturday afternoon. Draw a bar chart to show the results. 💬

Crispy pork	Beef noodles	Chicken curry	Chow mein	Chop suey
20	25	10	15	5

25
20
15
10
5
0

Marks: ☐ /1

2 On Sunday, there was double the number of orders for beef noodles. How many portions were served?

Answer: _____ Marks: ☐ /1

3 The least popular dish on Saturday was more popular on Sunday. 10 more were ordered. How many people ordered this dish on Sunday?

Answer: _____ Marks: ☐ /2

4 The crispy pork and chicken curry were in demand on Sunday. The combined number of orders was 50. If 31 people ordered the crispy pork, how many ordered the chicken curry?

Answer: _____ Marks: ☐ /3

Today's Marks: ☐ /7

Total Marks: ☐ /27 | I am happy with my work solving number stories. Yes ☐ No ☐

I would like to get better at _____

9 Money

We are learning to: Rename amounts of euro as cent and cent as euro. ☐ Add and subtract money. ☐

Day One Study the steps used to solve the problem in the example below.

Caroline went into the newsagent. She bought a new pencil costing 40c and a copybook costing 55c. How much money did she spend in total?

CLUEs

Circle the numbers and keywords:
  40c, 55c, bought, pencil, copybook, spend in total

Link with operation needed (+, −, × or ÷): **In total** means add (+).

Use a strategy: Make a table.

Estimate and calculate:

My estimate:
less than €1

H	T	U
	4	0
+	5	5
	9	5

Answer: 95c

Summarise and check how you got your answer:
  The pencil and copybook cost around €1, so I double-checked my answer to see if I was correct.

Try these.

CLUEs

1. Christopher loves swimming. He needs to buy a new cap for 550 cent and new goggles for 925 cent. How much will he spend altogether? Write the answer as euro and cent.

Answer: € _____   Marks: ___ /1

2. Ms Cambridge needs to fill up her reward-stickers jar. She buys smiley faces for 199 cent, gold stars for 150 cent and 'great work' stickers for 170 cent. How much does she spend altogether?

Answer: € _____   Marks: ___ /2

3. Abigail's mum wants to post a card and a large envelope. The stamp for the card costs 72c and the one for the large envelope costs 38c more. How much will she spend altogether?

Answer: € _____   Marks: ___ /3

Today's Marks: ___ /6

Day Two Try these.

1 Kids' Club films are shown each Saturday morning in the cinema. Cian bought a ticket for €4.30. If he paid with €5.00, how much change did he get?

> Remember: €1 = 100c

Answer: _____ **Marks:** ___ /1

2 Mrs Shields needed a new watch battery, so she headed to the jeweller's. She paid with €10.00 and the battery cost €5.50. How much change did she get?

> **Top tip:** The decimal point separates the euro from the cent.
> **€4.87**

Answer: _____ **Marks:** ___ /1

3 The dry-cleaners have two special offers at the moment: **(a)** 5 shirts dry-cleaned for €10 or **(b)** 12 shirts dry-cleaned for €20. Which deal is better value for money, **(a)** or **(b)**?

> **Top tip:** Make a table.

Answer: _____ **Marks:** ___ /2

4 The McHugh family ran out of burgers at their barbeque. Lou McHugh hurried to the butcher's and bought 6 burgers for €16.50. How much change did she get from €20?

Answer: _____ **Marks:** ___ /3

Today's Marks: ___ /7

Day Three Try these.

The local barber shop is very busy these days. The owner put a price list in the shop window for boys and their dads to see.

Barbara's Barber Shop Price List

Gent's dry cut	€9.50	Gent's wash, cut and blowdry	€11.00
Clipper cut	€8.50	Boy's cut (12 years or younger)	€8.50
OAP's dry cut	€8.00	OAP's wash, cut and blowdry	€9.50
Beard trim	€2.50	Standard shave	€10.00
Luxury shave	€20.00		

1 On Saturday morning, Noah and his dad headed to the barber's. Noah got the boy's cut and his dad got the gent's dry cut. How much did it cost for both?

Answer: Marks: /1

2 The principal of the local primary school decided to get a wash, cut and blowdry and a standard shave. How much did he spend?

Answer: Marks: /1

3 Noah's grandad is an old-age pensioner (OAP). He decided to go to the barber's too. He got the OAP's dry cut and a luxury shave and paid with a €50 note. How much change did he get?

Answer: Marks: /2

4 If **(a)** the gent's dry cut was increased by €2 and **(b)** the luxury shave was decreased by €5, how much would they each amount to then?

Answer: (a)   (b)   Marks: /3

Today's Marks: /7

Day Four Try these.

1 Football boots cost €42, football socks cost €6 and a jersey costs €28. How much do they cost altogether?

€42 €6 €28

Answer: _____ **Marks:** ___ /1

2 Brooke goes to the chemist to buy a first-aid kit for the under 12s camogie team. The first-aid kit costs €24.54. How much change does Brooke get from €30.00?

Answer: _____ **Marks:** ___ /2

3 Tara's mum wants to buy a new duvet set each for Tara and her sister. Tara would like an emojis duvet set costing €15.95 and her sister would like a ballerina duvet set costing €17.95. If their mum pays with €40.00, how much change will she get?

Answer: _____ **Marks:** ___ /3

Today's Marks: ___ /6

Puzzle power

a – €1	b – €2	c – €3	d – €4	e – €5	f – €6	g – €7	h – €8	i – €9
j – €10	k – €11	l – €12	m – €13	n – €14	o – €15	p – €16	q – €17	r – €18
s – €19	t – €20	u – €21	v – €22	w – €23	x – €24	y – €25	z – €26	

1. How much is the word 'coin' worth?
2. What is the value of your name?
3. Think of an expensive word and work out its value.

Example: 'treasure' = €107!

Duties

Reader
Calculator
Checker
Reporter

Total Marks: ___ /26 | **I still have a question about** _____

My favourite activity was _____

10 🐕 2-D Shapes

We are learning to: Identify 2-D shapes. ☐ Identify tessellating shapes. ☐
Identify the properties of a hexagon. ☐ Identify the use of 2-D shapes in the environment. ☐
Identify sides, angles, parallel and nonparallel lines of 2-D shapes. ☐

Day One | Study the steps used to solve the problem in the example below.

In a square, a circle and a triangle, how many edges are there altogether?

CLUES

Circle the numbers and keywords: square, circle, triangle, edges

Link with operation needed (+, −, × or ÷): **Altogether** means add (+).

Use a strategy: Act it out. ☐ ○ △

Estimate and calculate:

My estimate: 2 edges per shape, making 6

Count the edges; square 4, circle 1, triangle 3.
$4 + 1 + 3 = 8$

Answer: 8

Summarise and check how you got your answer:

I drew a diagram of the shapes and this helped me to identify and count the edges.

Remember: Edges are the same as sides.

Try these.

CLUES

1. How many edges are there in 4 semi-circles, 2 circles and 5 ovals?

Answer: _____ Marks: ☐ /1

2. In a modern-art painting, there are 2 of each of the following shapes: square, rectangle, triangle, circle, semi-circle and oval. How many vertices (corners) are there altogether?

Answer: _____ Marks: ☐ /2

3. William and his mum painted a border of shapes around his baby sister's cot. They painted 5 rectangles, 10 squares and 6 triangles. How many edges were there in the shapes altogether?

Answer: _____ Marks: ☐ /3

Strand: Shape and Space **Strand Unit:** 2-D Shapes

Today's Marks: ☐ /6

Day Two Try these.

Ms Black took her class of 24 pupils out to the yard. She gave each of them a long piece of string and told them, in groups, to use the string to make shapes.

1 How many pupils with 1 piece of string each were needed to make 3 squares?

Rhyme

2-D shapes have two dimensions,
Height and width and that is all.
They are flat and can be traced
On a piece of paper or on a wall.

Answer: _____ Marks: ____ /1

2 Ms Black organised the class into groups of 3 and told them to make triangles. How many triangles did they make altogether?

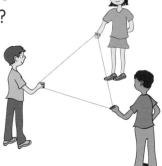

Answer: _____ Marks: ____ /1

3 **(a)** Ms Black organised the pupils into groups of 6 and told them to make a large beehive pattern. Each group needed to make a specific shape. What shape do you think this was?

(b) If 30 pupils from 4th Class joined Ms Black's class in making a beehive pattern with pieces of string, how many shapes did they make altogether?

Keywords

A **tessellation** is a pattern of shapes that fit together without overlapping or leaving gaps. Rectangles, squares and regular hexagons and triangles can tessellate.

Answers: (a) _____ (b) _____ Marks: ____ /2

4 **(a)** Finally, the pupils were allowed to make their own shapes with the string. What shapes could they have made? Draw some of them.

(b) How many four-sided shapes could 36 pupils have made?

Answers: (a) _____ (b) _____ Marks: ____ /3

Day Three · Try these.

1 Olivia is using a stick to draw 2-D shapes containing parallel lines in the snow. What shapes might she draw?

Answer: _____ Marks: ___ /1

2 A baker is assembling a train cake for a child's birthday. The cake will have an engine and two carriages. The baker will place 2 pairs of plastic sticks in parallel lines between the parts of the cake to join them together. How many plastic sticks will she need?

Answer: _____ Marks: ___ /1

3 Tom constructs picture frames for a living. A local gallery has asked him to construct frames for 7 paintings and 5 photographs. How many pairs of parallel lines will there be in these frames in total?

Answer: _____ Marks: ___ /2

4 There were 50 tiles on the roof of Jane's treehouse, but some of them blew off during a storm. If 38 tiles were still intact, how many pairs of parallel lines were lost during the storm?

Answer: _____ Marks: ___ /3

Super Sleuth challenge

On a sheet of paper, design a house using only 10 squares. You can rotate the squares to make diamond shapes if you like. Display your picture in the classroom.

Puzzle power

How many triangles do you see, 9, 10, 11, 12 or 13?

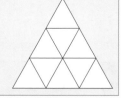

Today's Marks: ___ /7

Day Four Try these.

Draw the 2-D shapes in the table based on the clues given below.

First shape	Second shape	Third shape	Fourth shape	Fifth shape

1 The first and second shapes contain 10 edges in total. If you removed two edges from the first shape and drew a diagonal line, you would be left with a triangle. What are the shapes?

Answers: _____ and _____ Marks: ___ /1

2 The third shape has 1 curved edge and 1 straight edge. The third and fourth shapes have 5 edges between them. The fifth is shaped like a coin and has no vertices (corners). What are the shapes?

Answers: _____ and _____ and _____ Marks: ___ /2

3 Find the total **(a)** edges and **(b)** vertices in the five shapes above.

Answers: (a) _____ (b) _____ Marks: ___ /3

Today's Marks: ___ /6

Duties

Reader
Calculator
Checker
Reporter

Super Sleuth investigates

1. The image shows a mosaic made of ceramic tiles. Can you identify tessellating shapes in the design?

2. Where might you find a mosaic like this one?

3. Can you think of any maths questions based on the image?

Total Marks: ___ /26 | I feel confident about my work when _____

My teacher can help me by _____

11 Revision 2

On Safari

The McKenskey family were the lucky winners of a holiday in South Africa. The prize included a safari and a trip to a wildlife sanctuary.

Day One Try these.

1. On their first day on safari, the family saw a herd of 37 elephants. If 12 of them were calves (baby elephants), how many were adults?

Answer: _____ Marks: ___ /1

2. There were 145 wildebeests on the plain, but 39 left in search of water. How many wildebeests remained on the plain?

Answer: _____ Marks: ___ /1

3. There are two species of rhino in South Africa, the black rhino and the white rhino. The safari guide told the family that there were 685 white rhinos in the area, but only 297 black rhinos. What was the difference between their numbers?

Answer: _____ Marks: ___ /2

4. There was a total of 365 zebras and giraffes gathered drinking at a lake. 126 giraffes and 87 zebras wandered away to graze. How many zebras and giraffes were still drinking at the lake?

Answer: _____ Marks: ___ /3

Strand: Number **Strand Units:** Operations – subtraction
Strand: Data **Strand Unit:** Representing and Interpreting Data
Strand: Measures **Strand Unit:** Money **Strand:** Shape and Space **Strand Unit:** 2-D Shapes

Today's Marks: ___ /7

Day Two Try these.

Using the clues given below, fill in the graph.

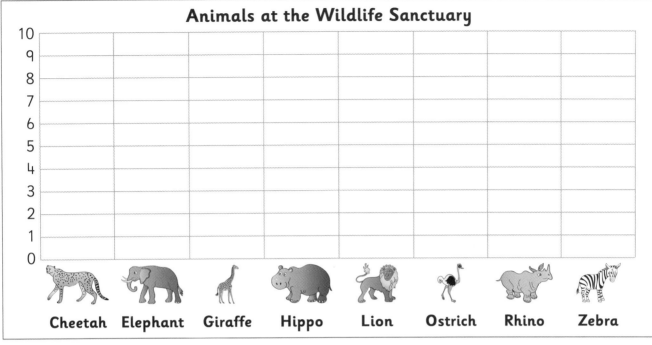

Animals at the Wildlife Sanctuary

Cheetah   Elephant   Giraffe   Hippo   Lion   Ostrich   Rhino   Zebra

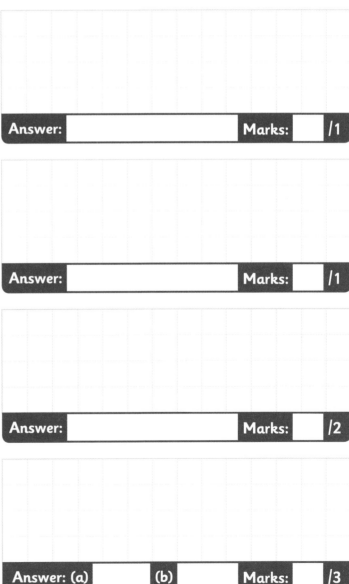

1 There were twice as many elephants as cheetahs at the wildlife sanctuary. If there were 5 cheetahs, how many elephants were there?

Answer: _____   Marks: ___ /1

2 The numbers of giraffes, lions and rhinos were 2 less than each other in that order. If there were 8 giraffes, how many lions and rhinos were there?

Answer: _____   Marks: ___ /1

3 The combined total of hippos, ostriches and zebras was 21. If there was an equal number in all three groups, how many of each were there?

Answer: _____   Marks: ___ /2

4 (a) How many animals were there altogether in the sanctuary?
(b) If double that number of animals was added, how many **extra** animals would there be?

Answer: (a) _____ (b) _____   Marks: ___ /3

Day Three Try these.

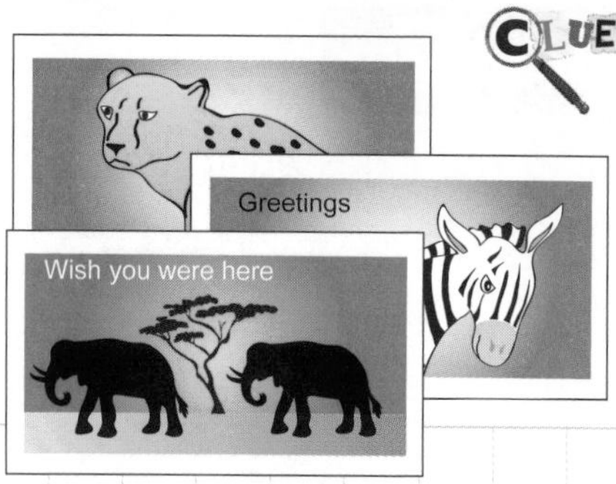

1 The currency of South Africa is the rand (R). It cost R1.50 for a postcard at the wildlife sanctuary. If the family bought 3 postcards, how much did they spend?

CLUES

Greetings

Wish you were here

Top tip:
Identify a pattern.

Answer: _____ Marks: ___ /1

2 A framed photograph taken on safari cost R15.70. If Mr McKenskey paid R20.00, how much change did he receive?

Answer: _____ Marks: ___ /1

3 Tanya McKenskey bought two souvenirs for her friends at the wildlife sanctuary. She bought a charm bracelet costing R4.35 and a lion key ring costing R3.80. How much change did she get from R10.00?

Answer: _____ Marks: ___ /2

4 If a one-day safari costs R50.25 per adult and R32.50 per child, how much would it cost for the McKenskey family (2 adults and 2 children)?

Answer: _____ Marks: ___ /3

Today's Marks: ___ /7

Day Four Try these.

Top tip: Make a table.

CLUEs

1 At the entrance to the safari park, Josh McKenskey noticed 3 **rectangular** signs with safety warnings for visitors. How many **(a)** vertices and **(b)** parallel lines were in these 3 signs?

Answers: (a) _____ (b) _____ Marks: ___ /1

2 Josh saw 9 more signs at the safari park, each with a red circular 'warning' symbol. How many edges were there in total on all of the red circles that Josh saw?

Answer: _____ Marks: ___ /2

3 The McKenskey family used binoculars to get a better view of the animals. The binoculars were fixed to the jeep and they had to insert a **hexagon**-shaped token into a slot to release each pair. They bought 5 tokens costing R2.00 each.

(a) How many edges were on the 5 tokens?

(b) How much did they cost?

Binoculars

Answers: (a) _____ (b) _____ Marks: ___ /3

Today's Marks: ___ /6

Duties

Reader

Calculator

Checker

Reporter

Puzzle power

It is a good idea for a safari jeep to have a camouflage pattern. What tessellating shapes could you use so that there would not be any gaps in the pattern? Discuss your answers.

Super Sleuth investigates

1. What types of line can you identify in the image of the jeep above?

2. Can you think of any maths questions based on the image?

12  Strategy: Identifying Patterns

Day One

Identifying patterns is a problem-solving strategy that involves looking at how shapes, objects, pictures or numbers are repeated in a number story.

💬 Look at this pattern and say the colours out loud: ●◆◆●●◆◆●

There are three terms in the core of the pattern – **green**, **blue**, **red**. The core is the shortest list of colours that you can say before the list repeats.

The next four terms of this pattern would be would be **green**, **blue**, **red**, **green**.

Being able to skip count forwards and backwards will help you to find missing terms in a number sequence. Read the following number sequence:

$$15, \quad 20, \quad 25, \quad 30, \quad \_\_\_, \quad \_\_\_, \quad \_\_\_$$

(+5) (+5) (+5) (+5) (+5) (+5)

The **rule** of this number sequence is **+5**. What are the next three terms?

Try these.

CLUES

1) Maisie was making a bracelet. She threaded beads in the following order: 1 blue, 1 red, 1 green, 2 blue, 2 red, 2 green. Then, she began the same sequence all over again. Use your colours to draw the core of the pattern.

Marks: ☐ /1

2) Maisie used 9 beads to create the core of the pattern above. If the bracelet contained 36 beads, how many times did the core appear?

Answer: _____ Marks: ☐ /2

3) Maisie decided to make a necklace to go with her bracelet, but this time, after using 2 of every colour, she went up to 3 and so on. How many beads did she use if she went up to 5 of every colour?

Answer: _____ Marks: ☐ /3

Today's Marks: ☐ /6

Day Two Try these.

Use the strategy of identifying patterns to solve each number story below.

① Melanie bought a wallpaper border from a hardware shop for her baby's bedroom. The border had the pattern shown below. Draw the next 4 terms in this pattern. Say the words out loud to help you. 💬

Marks: ☐ /1

② How many shapes does the core of the pattern in the border above contain?

Answer: ☐ Marks: ☐ /1

③ Melanie saw another border at the hardware shop, but this one had the pattern shown below. Draw the next 5 terms in this pattern.

Marks: ☐ /2

④ Design your own pattern with 25 terms using the sun, moon and star pictures.

Marks: ☐ /3

Today's Marks: ☐ /7

Day Three Try these.

Use the strategy of identifying patterns to solve each number story below.

Use the following number sequence to answer the questions below:

2 cm, 4 cm, 8 cm, 14 cm, 22 cm, 32 cm, __ cm, 58 cm

1 **(a)** What is the rule of the number sequence above? **(b)** What is the missing number?

Sequence:

3, 5, 7, 9, ...

1st term 2nd term 3rd term 4th term Three dots means goes on forever (infinite).

Answers: **(a)** _____ **(b)** _____ Marks: ___ /1

2 What are the next 3 terms of the blue number sequence above?

Answer: _____ Marks: ___ /1

3 If the blue number sequence above represents the height of a sunflower plant over 8 weeks, how tall was the plant in the fifth week?

Answer: _____ Marks: ___ /2

4 If there is another sunflower plant growing at a different rate from the one above, can you and your partner think of a different sequence to show the rate of growth over 5 weeks?

Answer: _____ Marks: ___ /3

Today's Marks: ___ /7

Day Four Try these.

Use the strategy of identifying patterns to solve each number story below.

① Leeroy is making up party bags for his birthday party. He places 2 cola bottles in the first bag, 4 in the second, 6 in the third and 8 in the fourth. How many cola bottles will he place in the sixth bag? Explain your answer.

Answer: _____ Marks: ☐ /1

② There were 20 guests at Leeroy's party. They decided to play musical chairs. There were 20 chairs and every time the music stopped, they took away 2 chairs. How many times will the music have to stop for there to be no chairs left?

Answer: _____ Marks: ☐ /2

③ There were 33 jelly babies in a bowl on the table. The children who liked jelly babies took 3 each until there were none left. How many children liked jelly babies?

Answer: _____ Marks: ☐ /3

Today's Marks: ☐ /6

Total Marks: ☐ /26 | What strategy did I learn this week? _____

My favourite activity was _____

13  Multiplication

We are learning to: Understand multiplication as repeated addition and vice versa. ☐
Explore, understand and apply the zero, commutative and distributive properties of multiplication. ☐
Develop and/or recall multiplication facts within 100. ☐ Multiply a one-digit or two-digit number by 0–10. ☐

Day One — Study the steps used to solve the problem in the example below.

There are 2 bags in the soccer clubhouse. Each bag contains 5 water bottles. How many water bottles are there altogether?

Circle the numbers and keywords:
  2 bags, 5 water bottles, altogether

Link with operation needed (+, −, × or ÷): Multiply (×).

Use a strategy: Visualise.

Estimate and calculate:
  My estimate:
  2 groups of 5 = 10

2 × 5 = 10

Answer:
10

Summarise and check how you got your answer:
  There are 2 groups of 5 water bottles. I drew a picture to help me check if the answer was correct.

Try these using repeated addition.

(1) An orchestra had 6 violins that each needed 2 new strings. How many new strings were needed in total?

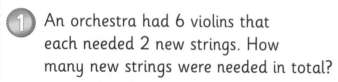

Answer: _____ Marks: ___ /1

(2) Matthew and his friends made up a basketball game at yard time. Each basket scored was worth 10 points. Matthew's team scored 6 baskets and the other team scored 8 baskets. What was the difference between their scores?

Answer: _____ Marks: ___ /2

(3) In a theme park, the motion base ride was full. It had 3 rows of seats with 5 seats in each row. When the ride ended, 8 of the people who got off bought another ticket. How many people did not buy another ticket?

Answer: _____ Marks: ___ /3

Today's Marks: ____ /6

Day Two   Try these.

1 Leon's gran brought 2 packets of muffins at the bakery. There were 4 muffins in each packet. How many muffins did she buy altogether?

> **Top tip:**
> Act it out.

Answer: _____   **Marks:** ___ /1

2 Fiona has 4 times as many hair slides as her sister Faye. If Faye has 8 hair slides, how many does Fiona have?

Answer: _____   **Marks:** ___ /1

Remember: There are different ways to work out a multiplication number story.

Mystery number: Have a go!
Twice the product of 3 × 5 is three times as great as the mystery number. What is the mystery number?

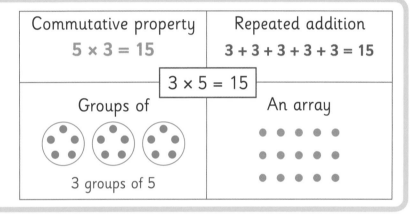

Commutative property	Repeated addition
5 × 3 = 15	3 + 3 + 3 + 3 + 3 = 15

3 × 5 = 15

Groups of	An array
3 groups of 5	

3 At the Splash Swimming Club, every child needs 2 swim caps in case one rips. If there are 10 members in the under-10s class, how many swim caps do they have in total?

Answer: _____   **Marks:** ___ /2

4 A magician is performing a trick. He places four cups upside-down on a table. He places three balls beneath one cup. He says 'abracadabra' and then taps each of the four cups with his magic wand. He lifts the cups and suddenly there are three balls beneath each cup! How many balls are there then?

Answer: _____   **Marks:** ___ /3

Today's Marks: ___ /7

Day Three Try these.

CLUES

1. The little bumps on top of Lego bricks are called studs. These are what make Lego bricks join together. How many studs would there be on 2 of the bricks shown?

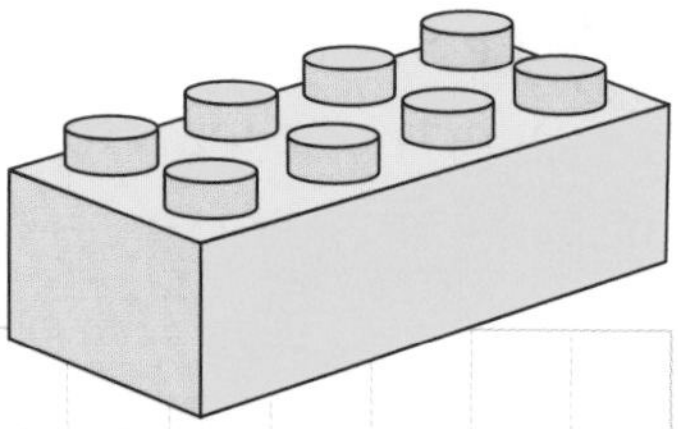

Answer: _____   Marks: [ ] /1

2. In a Lego pirates set, there are 3 times as many green bricks as yellow bricks. If there are 9 yellow bricks, how many green bricks are there?

Top tip:
Identify a pattern.

Answer: _____   Marks: [ ] /1

3. Chloe is building a hospital for her Lego city. She has already used 5 packets of 9 black bricks. If there are 63 black bricks in total in the set, how many has she got left to use?

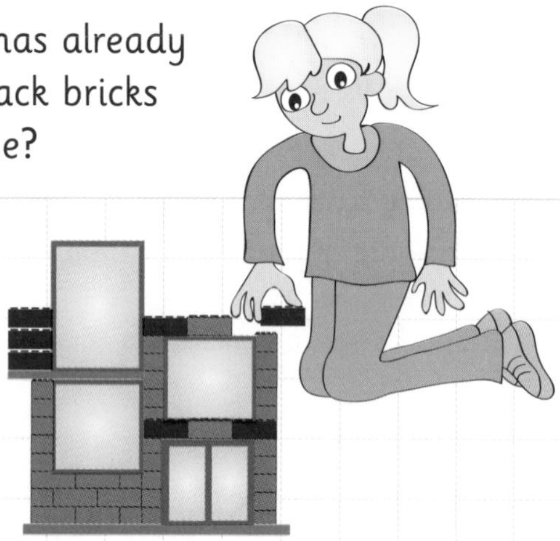

Answer: _____   Marks: [ ] /2

Duties
Reader
Calculator
Checker
Reporter

4. Toby is creating a design on his Lego baseplate. He plans to use 4 blue bricks. He will use double the amount of orange bricks as blue bricks. He will use triple the amount of red bricks as orange bricks. How many bricks will he use in total?

Top tip:
Make a table.

Answer: _____   Marks: [ ] /3

Today's Marks: [ ] /7

Day Four Try these.

 1 A chef is preparing meatball kebabs for a barbeque. He has 56 meatballs and 7 kebab skewers. How many meatballs should he put on each skewer? Write the multiplication sentence.

> **Top tip:**
> Work backwards.

Answer: _____ **Marks:** ☐ /1

2 Miranda loves writing. Every week, she writes 2 new stories. Each story is 4 pages long. How many pages will she have written after 6 weeks?

Answer: _____ **Marks:** ☐ /2

 3 The windows of an office building need to be cleaned. Half of them will be cleaned today. If there are 4 × 5 windows at the front of the building and 4 × 8 at the back of the building, how many will be cleaned today?

Answer: _____ **Marks:** ☐ /3

Today's Marks: ☐ /6

Puzzle power

Use the magic multiplication grid to answer the questions.

1. 8 × 5 =

2. 6 × 8 =

3. 4 × 9 =

4. 7 × 9 =

5. 12 × 5 =

6. 8 × 9 =

7. 12 × 7 =

8. 11 × 12 =

X	1	2	3	4	5	6	7	8	9	10	11	12
1	1	2	3	4	5	6	7	8	9	10	11	12
2	2	4	6	8	10	12	14	16	18	20	22	24
3	3	6	9	12	15	18	21	24	27	30	33	36
4	4	8	12	16	20	24	28	32	36	40	44	48
5	5	10	15	20	25	30	35	40	45	50	55	60
6	6	12	18	24	30	36	42	48	54	60	66	72
7	7	14	21	28	35	42	49	56	63	70	77	84
8	8	16	24	32	40	48	56	64	72	80	88	96
9	9	18	27	36	45	54	63	72	81	90	99	108
10	10	20	30	40	50	60	70	80	90	100	110	120
11	11	22	33	44	55	66	77	88	99	110	121	132
12	12	24	36	48	60	72	84	96	108	120	132	144

Total Marks: ☐ /26 | I understand more about _____

I would like to get better at _____

14  Fractions

We are learning to: Identify halves, quarters, eighths and tenths. ☐ Calculate a fraction of a set. ☐ Name equivalent fractions. ☐ Understand the relationship between fractions and division. ☐ Compare and order fractions. ☐

Day One Study the steps used to solve the problem in the example below.

Joshua took his birthday cake to school to share with his peers. If they ate $\frac{3}{4}$ of it, how much was left?

CLUES

Circle the numbers and keywords: $\frac{3}{4}$, cake, ate, left

Link with operation needed (+, −, × or ÷):
How much was left? means take away (−).

Use a strategy: Visualise a cake cut into 4 quarters.

Estimate and calculate:
I know that there are 4 quarters in a unit.

$$4 - 3 = 1$$

Answer:
1 quarter ($\frac{1}{4}$)

Summarise and check how you got your answer:
I know that there are 4 quarters in a unit, so if they ate 3 quarters, 1 quarter was left over.

Try these.   **CLUES**

1 Ben ordered a Nutella crêpe. He watched the chef fold it in half and then fold it again. What fraction had she folded it into?

$\frac{4}{4}$ $\frac{3}{4}$ $\frac{2}{4}$ $\frac{7}{7}$

Answer: $\frac{1}{4}$ **Marks:** /1

2 3rd Class need to practise for the Spelling Bee. They learn $\frac{1}{8}$ of their spellings list per night. If they practise from Monday to Thursday, what fraction of the spellings list will they have learned?

$\frac{1}{4}$ $\frac{1}{4}$

$\frac{1}{8}$ $\frac{1}{8}$ $\frac{1}{8}$ $\frac{1}{8}$

Answer: $\frac{1}{2}$ **Marks:** /2

3 Callum and Lorcan were given pocket money by their mum. If Callum spent half of his pocket money and Lorcan spent only half of what Callum spent, what fraction of his pocket money did Lorcan spend?

C $\frac{1}{2}$ L $\frac{1}{2} - \frac{1}{2}$ of $\frac{1}{2} = \frac{1}{4}$

Answer: $\frac{1}{4}$ **Marks:** /3

Today's Marks: /6

Day Two Try these.

1			
$\frac{1}{2}$		$\frac{1}{2}$	
$\frac{1}{4}$	$\frac{1}{4}$	$\frac{1}{4}$	$\frac{1}{4}$

$\frac{1}{8}$	$\frac{1}{8}$	$\frac{1}{8}$	$\frac{1}{8}$	$\frac{1}{8}$	$\frac{1}{8}$	$\frac{1}{8}$	$\frac{1}{8}$
$\frac{1}{10}$	$\frac{1}{10}$	$\frac{1}{10}$	$\frac{1}{10}$	$\frac{1}{10}$	$\frac{1}{10}$	$\frac{1}{10}$	$\frac{1}{10}$	$\frac{1}{10}$	$\frac{1}{10}$

1 Callum and Lorcan saved up their pocket money and treated themselves and their mum to lunch in a delicatessen. Callum ordered a chicken roll and cut it into two equal pieces. What fraction did one piece represent?

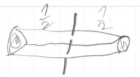

Answer: $\frac{1}{2}$ Marks: ☐ /1

2 Callum and Lorcan's mum ordered $\frac{1}{2}$ a tub of coleslaw to take home from the delicatessen. She then decided that she wanted $\frac{2}{8}$ more coleslaw. What fraction of the tub was full?

$$\frac{1}{2} + \frac{2}{8} = \frac{3}{4}$$

Answer: $\frac{3}{4}$ Marks: ☐ /1

3 Shauna used $\frac{5}{10}$ of a banana in a smoothie. She spread $\frac{2}{8}$ of it on a slice of brown bread and gave the rest of it to her dog. What fraction of the banana did she give to her dog?

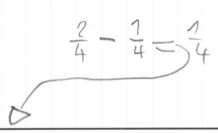

$$\frac{2}{4} - \frac{1}{4} = \frac{1}{4}$$

Answer: $\frac{1}{4}$ Marks: ☐ /2

4 The Hugh family ordered a cheese pizza and a pepperoni pizza from the local pizzeria. Scott Hugh and his dad went to collect them, but they were so hungry that they ate $\frac{1}{4}$ of the cheese pizza and $\frac{1}{2}$ of the pepperoni pizza in the car on the way home. What fraction of the pizzas was left for the rest of the family?

pepperoni = $\frac{1}{2}$ left
cheese = $\frac{3}{4}$ left

$$\frac{1}{2} + \frac{3}{4} = 1\frac{?}{4}$$

Answer: $1\frac{?}{4}$ Marks: ☐ /3

Today's Marks: ☐ /7   **61**

Day Three Try these.

1 A clothes shop is having a sale on Saturday. Help the shop assistant to calculate the discount and sale price for each item.

Item	Original Price	Discount		Sale Price
Jumper	€20.00	$\frac{1}{10}$	€2.00	€18.00
T-shirt	€10.00	$\frac{1}{10}$	€1.00	€9.00
Shorts	€15.00	$\frac{1}{10}$	€1.50	€13.50
Jacket	€100.00	$\frac{1}{10}$	€10.00	€90.00
Dress	€50.00	$\frac{1}{10}$	€5.00	€45.00
Trousers	€60.00	$\frac{1}{10}$	€6.00	€54.00

[handwritten working:]
original price
€57.00
→ 57 − 5 = 52

Marks: ☐ /1

2 **(a)** There were 10 jumpers on sale and $\frac{1}{2}$ of them were sold. How many jumpers were **sold**? **(b)** There were 16 T-shirts on sale $\frac{1}{4}$ of them were sold. How many of T-shirts were left?

[handwritten working:]
10 − 5 = 5   16 − 4 = 12

Answers: (a) 5   **(b)** 12   **Marks:** ☐ /1

3 There were 48 jackets on sale and $\frac{1}{4}$ out of them were sold. $\frac{1}{2}$ of the jackets sold were red and the other $\frac{1}{2}$ were blue. How many blue jackets were sold?

[handwritten working:]
12 − 6 = 6

Answer: 6   **Marks:** ☐ /2

4 There were 8 children at a birthday party. All of the children got an equal amount of treats, so they each got $\frac{1}{8}$ of everything. There were 16 bars of chocolate, 24 packets of jellies and 8 lollipops. How many of each treat did each child get?

[handwritten working:]
1 lollipop
2 bars
3 jellies

Answer: They all got 6 treats.   **Marks:** ☐ /3

Today's Marks: ☐ /7

Day Four Try these.

1. A sneeze can travel at a speed of 100 km per hour! If the speed was reduced by $\frac{1}{2}$, at what speed would a sneeze travel?

Top tip: Make a table.

$$100 - \frac{1}{2} = 50$$

Answer: 50 km **Marks:** /1

2. It is estimated that our eyes blink 5 times every $\frac{1}{4}$ of a minute. At this rate, how many times do they blink in **(a)** one minute and **(b)** 10 minutes?

Answers: (a) 20 **(b)** 100 **Marks:** /2

3. It is estimated that a snake spends only $\frac{1}{4}$ of its life awake!
   (a) For how many hours is it awake each day (24 hours)?
   (b) For how many hours is it awake each week?

Answers: (a) 6 hrs **(b)** 42 hrs **Marks:** /3

Today's Marks: /6

Puzzle power

Find the answers to the fractions puzzle. Then, fill in the blank template and have your friend work out the answers.

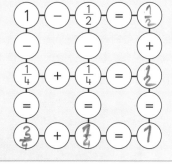

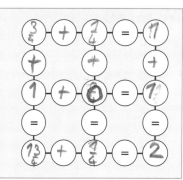

Duties

Reader
Calculator
Checker
Reporter

Super Sleuth investigates

1. What fraction of the T-shirts are stripy? $\frac{1}{2}$

2. What fraction of the T-shirts have a picture of a superhero? $\frac{3}{4}$

3. What fraction of the T-shirts are plain? $\frac{1}{4}$

4. With your partner, make up 3 questions using fractions based on the image.

Total Marks: /26 | **I understand more about**

What I found hardest was

15 Length

We are learning to: Estimate, compare, measure and record lengths. ☐ Rename units of length in m and cm. ☐ Measure length in metres and centimetres. ☐ Add and subtract metres and centimetres. ☐

Day One Study the steps used to solve the problem in the example below.

Jamie's clothes line measures 2 m 43 cm in length. Amy's clothes line measures 2 m 21 cm in length. What length are they altogether?

CLUES

Circle the numbers and keywords:
    2 m 43 cm, 2 m 21 cm, length, altogether

Link with operation needed (+, −, × or ÷):
    Altogether means add (+).

Use a strategy: Visualise.

Estimate and calculate:
My estimate: 2 + 2 = 4,
so more than 4

m	cm
2	43
+ 2	21
4	64

Answer:
4 m 64 cm

Top tip: Line up the metres under the metres and the centimetres under the centimetres when adding or subtracting to get the correct answer.

Summarise and check how you got your answer:
    I added the length of the two clothes lines to get the combined length of both.

Try these.

Top tip: Act it out.

CLUES

1. Rachel made a bracelet, a necklace and a ring using loom bands. The bracelet was 22 cm long, the necklace was 46 cm long and the ring was 14 cm long. How long were they in total?

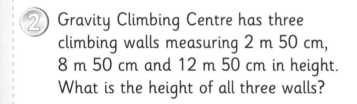

Answer: 82 cm   Marks: /1

2. Gravity Climbing Centre has three climbing walls measuring 2 m 50 cm, 8 m 50 cm and 12 m 50 cm in height. What is the height of all three walls?

Answer: 23 m 50 cm   Marks: /2

3. A train carriage is 23 m 43 cm long. Three carriages are needed on the Cork to Cobh train. What is the combined length of the three carriages?

×3 ≈ 69 m

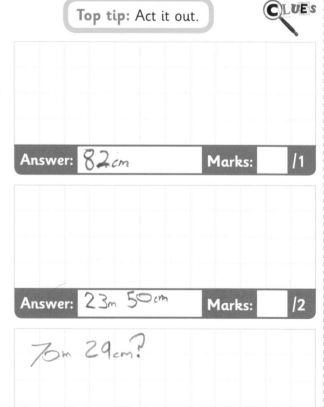

70 m 29 cm?

Answer: 70 m 29 cm   Marks: /3

Today's Marks: /6

Day Two Try these.

1 Cormac uses a 71 cm hurley to play hurling. His brother uses a 96 cm hurley. What is the difference between the two sizes? 💬

Answer: 15cm   **Marks:** /1

Top tip:
A fingernail is about 1 cm wide.
A guitar is about 1 m long.

1 cm

1 m

100 cm = 1 m

2 A player at a Gaelic football match took a free kick 65 m from the goal. How far away from the 45 m line was she?

Answer: 20m   **Marks:** /1

3 The Ha'penny Bridge in Dublin is 43 m long. The Samuel Beckett Bridge is 120 m long. What is the difference between the two lengths?

Answer: 77m   **Marks:** /2

4 A dressmaker ordered fabric online measuring 34 m in length. At first, she cut off 12 m 50 cm to make a pair of curtains and then, she cut off 8 m 40 cm to make cushion covers. How much fabric was left?

(she used 20m 90cm.)

Answer: 13m 10cm   **Marks:** /3

Super Sleuth challenge

In your copybook, draw a shape that is 20 cm long. Use a ruler to help you.

Joke!
Who is the king of the pencil case?
The ruler!

Today's Marks: /7

Day Three Try these.

A rowing club meets every Sunday. Some of the members row independently, while others row in pairs or groups. Below is a list of the boats available.

Single scull	Double scull	Quadruple scull
Length: 8 m 20 cm	Length: 10 m 40 cm	Length: 13 m 40 cm
Two are available.	Four are available.	Four are available.

1. There are two single sculls. What is the combined length of the single sculls when placed end to end?

Answer: 16m 40 cm   **Marks:** /1

2. There are four double sculls. On competition day, a club official needs to wax all of the double sculls. What is the combined length that he needs to wax?

Answer: 41m 60 cm   **Marks:** /1

3. The quadruple scull is the longest boat. What is the difference in length between this boat and the shortest boat?

Answer: 5m 20 cm   **Marks:** /2

4. There are four quadruple sculls. A club official needs to cover them up with plastic sheeting while the clubhouse is being painted. What is the mininum length of plastic sheeting that she will need to cover all four of the quadruple sculls?

Top tip: Make a table.

Answer: 3 9m 60 cm   **Marks:** /3

Today's Marks: /7

Day Four Try these.

1 At a skipping competition, there were four skipping ropes measuring 213 cm, 243 cm, 274 cm and 304 cm. Record the combined length of the two middle-sized ropes.

Answer: 3m 17cm   **Marks:** /1

2 Eddie planned to join an astronomy club, so he bought a new telescope measuring 70 cm in length. When he arrived at the club, he realised that he had bought the wrong one. The tutor said that he needed one measuring 1.4 m. How much shorter was Eddie's telescope?

Answer: 30.4 cm   **Marks:** /2

3 Three diving boards are being installed at a new swimming pool. They measure 3 m 10 cm, 2 m 29 cm and 500 cm. What is their combined length?

Answer: 10m 39cm   **Marks:** /3

Today's Marks: /6

Duties

Reader
Calculator
Checker
Reporter

Super Sleuth investigates

Fact: Xie Qiuping from China has been growing her hair since 1973 from the age of 13. She holds the Guinness World Record for the longest hair (female) with a length of over 5 m 60 cm.

1. When you go to the hairdresser, how much hair do you think is cut off, m or cm?

2. How quickly does your hair grow? Use your ruler to estimate how much it grows per month.

Total Marks: /26 | **What strategy did I learn this week?**

When I begin a new number story, I

16 Chance

We are learning to: Use the language of chance. ☐ Identify the likelihood of something happening. ☐

Day One   Study the steps used to solve the problem in the example below.

Hawaii is located in the tropics, a region that is warm all year round. Based on this information, how likely is the following statement to be true?

It will snow tomorrow in Hawaii.

CLUEs

Keywords

Chance means the possibility of something happening. **The odds** is another way of saying it, e.g. The odds are high that is will rain today, so bring your umbrella.

Circle the numbers and keywords:
Hawaii, tropics, snow

Link with operation needed (+, −, × or ÷): None

Use a strategy: Visualise.

Estimate and calculate:

My estimate: It isn't likely to snow in a warm region.	Chance of it snowing? Unlikely	**Answer:** Unlikely

Summarise and check how you got your answer:
I know that Hawaii is near the Equator, where it is always warm, so it is unlikely to snow.

Try these.

1. What are the chances that Ben will win an Oscar for his performance in the school musical? Possible, impossible, likely, unlikely or certain?

Answer: _____ Marks: ☐ /1

2. Francis buys a lottery ticket every Wednesday and Saturday. What are the chances that she will win the jackpot? Possible, impossible, likely, unlikely or certain?

Answer: _____ Marks: ☐ /2

3. There are four seasons in a year. Niamh wishes for winter to be eliminated next year. What are chances that we will still have winter next year? Possible, impossible, likely, unlikely or certain?

Answer: _____ Marks: ☐ /3

Today's Marks: ☐ /6

Day Two Try these.

1 Keith has a key ring with three keys: one to his house, one to his gran's house and one to his aunt's house. What are the chances of Keith being able to open the door to the school with his keys? Possible, impossible, likely, unlikely or certain?

Answer: **Marks:** /1

2 Snooker is played using 22 balls as follows: 1 white cue ball, 15 reds, 1 yellow, 1 green, 1 brown, 1 blue, 1 pink and 1 black. What are the chances of potting a purple ball? Possible, impossible, likely, unlikely or certain?

Answer: **Marks:** /1

3 Manchester United are top of the Premier League with 81 points. They have not lost a game all season. They have a very good manager and even better players. What are the chances of them winning the final? Possible, impossible, likely, unlikely or certain?

Answer: **Marks:** /2

4 A new housing estate containing 125 bungalows is being built in town. What are the chances of the houses having a staircase? Possible, impossible, likely, unlikely or certain?

Answer: **Marks:** /3

Super Sleuth challenge

By tossing a pair of dice, work out the odds of:

Top tip: Make a table.

- rolling a 1.
- rolling a 3.
- rolling an odd number.
- rolling a number greater than 5.

Top tip: It is possible to predict the odds (chances) of an event by repeating an experiment several times. The results of the experiment can help you to think about why the results happened. You can also use the results to predict the chances of other events that are related, i.e. following a pattern.

Today's Marks: /7

Day Three   Try these.

1. The Morgan family went to a funfair. Finbarr Morgan played the coconut shy game. He had 3 attempts to knock the coconut off the stand with a wooden ball. What were his chances of knocking down the coconut? Possible, impossible, likely, unlikely or certain?

Answer: _____ **Marks:** ☐ /1

2. Sarah Morgan tried to win a large teddy at the hoopla game. She had 4 attempts to throw a rubber ring around the teddy. What were her chances of ringing the prize? Possible, impossible, likely, unlikely or certain?

Answer: _____ **Marks:** ☐ /1

3. Mrs Morgan discovered that her purse was open and all of her change had spilled into her handbag. She definitely remembered seeing a €2 coin in her purse earlier that day. What were the chances that she would find the €2 coin? Possible, impossible, likely, unlikely or certain?

Answer: _____ **Marks:** ☐ /2

4. There were a number of activities involving animals at the funfair, including a talented pets competition. Malcolm Morgan heard a little girl say that she was going to enter her pet alligator into the competition. What do you think were the chances that the girl really had a pet alligator and that it would have been allowed into the funfair? Explain your answer.

Answer: _____
_____
_____
_____
_____
_____

Marks: ☐ /3

Today's Marks: ☐ /7

Day Four Try these.

 1 There are 100 vehicles in a shopping centre car park. There are 50 cars, 30 vans and the rest are lorries. What are the chances of a spaceship leaving the car park?

Answer: **Marks:** /1

 2 Eleanor loves dunking her rich tea biscuits into her tea. Grace loves dunking her digestive biscuits into her tea. What are the chances that Eleanor's biscuit will fall into her teacup?

Answer: **Marks:** /2

3 Imagine a game in which six beads numbered 1 to 6 are placed in a bag. You have to take out a bead, check the number and then guess whether the next bead will have a higher or lower number and so on.

(a) The first bead is 6. What are the chances of the second bead being lower than 6?

(b) The second bead is 1. What are the chances of the third bead being lower than 2?

(c) The third bead is 4. What are the chances of the fourth bead being higher than 4?

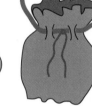

Answers: (a)   **(b)**   **(c)**   **Marks:** /3

Today's Marks: /6

Duties

Reader
Calculator
Checker
Reporter

Super Sleuth investigates

Write a list of events that are impossible.

Example: A horse will fly into my back garden.

Total Marks: /26   New words I've learned:

I would like to do chance questions about

17 Revision 3

Day One | The Racing Festival

Try these.

1. Pam entered her 5 racehorses in a racing festival. Each horse ran 3 races, but none of them ran in the same race. In how many races did Pam have a horse running in total?

Answer: _____ Marks: ___ /1

2. Every jockey was sponsored 2 free pairs of riding boots at the festival. If there were 10 jockeys, how many pairs of boots were given out?

Answer: _____ Marks: ___ /1

3. 8 racehorses need to have all 4 of their horseshoes replaced before the races begin. How many hooves will the farrier need to shoe altogether?

Answer: _____ Marks: ___ /2

4. A horse breeder bought a racehorse for €500. He later sold it for €600. He bought it back for €700 and then sold it again for €800. Did the breeder make money, lose money or break even? Explain your answer. 💬

> **Top tip:**
> Simplify.

Answer: _____ Marks: ___ /3

Strand: Number Strand Units: Operations – multiplication; Fractions
Strand: Measures Strand Unit: Length Strand: Data Strand Unit: Chance

Today's Marks: ___ /7

Day Two Try these.

1 Jonathan bought 20 apples for his horse in case she was hungry. He put $\frac{1}{2}$ of them in the horse's nosebag. How many apples did he put in the nosebag?

Answer: _____ Marks: ___ /1

2 Racehorses have a lifespan of around 24 years. They race while they are young and it is said that they are at their fastest when they are $\frac{1}{8}$ of the way into their lifespan. Can you calculate the age when a racehorse is fastest?

Answer: _____ Marks: ___ /1

3 There are 205 bones in the skeleton of a horse, with 20 bones in each leg. A horse named Celtic Charm fell during a race and the vet was worried that he might have broken $\frac{1}{4}$ of the bones in his front leg. How many bones was this?

Answer: _____ Marks: ___ /2

4 If a horse is galloping at a speed of 44 km per hour, how many kilometres will it travel in $\frac{1}{4}$ of an hour?

Top tip: Make a table.

Answer: _____ Marks: ___ /3

Today's Marks: ___ /7

Day Three Try these.

1 Ace Diamond, a pretty chestnut mare, measures 157 cm in height. Fox Trot, a handsome black stallion, measures 173 cm in height. What is the difference between their heights?

Answer: Marks: /1

2 Celtic Charm, Ace Diamond and Fox Trot each have a tail long enough to plait! What is the combined length of their tails if they measure 67 cm, 84 cm and 75 cm?

Answer: Marks: /1

3 A horse's eyes are bigger than those of any other land mammal. If **one eye** is 5 cm wide, what would 5 **pairs of eyes** measure?

Answer: Marks: /2

4 A pony measures around 140 cm in height, while a miniature horse measures around 76 cm in height. What is the difference between the height of a pony and the height of a miniature horse?

Answer: Marks: /3

Today's Marks: /7

Day Four Try these.

1 The first race on Saturday will start at 12:15 pm. Bobby and his friends are playing a match on Saturday, which will kick off at 12:30 pm. What are the chances that they will make it to the racecourse in time to see the first race? Possible, impossible, likely, unlikely or certain?

Answer: **Marks:** /1

2 What are the chances that it will rain on Saturday if it rains all day on Wednesday, Thursday and Friday? Possible, impossible, likely, unlikely or certain?

Answer: **Marks:** /2

3 There are 20 horses, including Ace Diamond, running in the Irish Grand National. What are the chances of Ace Diamond winning if she has come first in her previous 5 races? Possible, impossible, likely, unlikely or certain?

Answer: **Marks:** /3

Today's Marks: /6

Duties

Reader
Calculator
Checker
Reporter

Super Sleuth investigates

1. What fraction of the jockeys are wearing something red?
2. What are the chances of the race not starting?
3. Can you think of any maths questions based on the image?

18 Strategy: Visualising

Day One

Visualising is a problem-solving strategy in which you create an image of the number story that you are trying to solve. This might involve drawing a diagram or using a bar model, a number line or a table to put yourself in the situation. The skills associated with visualising include:

- internalising – closing your eyes and seeing the question in your mind.
- identifying – thinking of a useful image that you understand.
- comparing – scrutinising different images to see what is the same and what is different.
- connecting – remembering a topic that you have learned.
- sharing – describing the situation to one another.

There are 5 hamburgers and you eat 1. How many are left?

Try these.

 Today, we will draw a diagram to help us visualise each number story.

CLUES

1. At the Grand Grub Restaurant, the chef made six lemon drizzle cakes and placed lemon slices on top of each for decoration. How many lemon slices did he put on each cake if he wanted to use 12 in total? Draw a diagram.

Answer: _____ Marks: ___ /1

2. There are 24 waiters employed at the restaurant. Half of them are working, one-quarter of them have the day off and one-quarter are on a training course. How many waiters are on a training course? Draw a diagram.

Answer: _____ Marks: ___ /2

3. 3 steaks fit to a pan at the restaurant. If there are plenty of pans and the cooker has 8 rings, how many steaks can be cooked at the same time? Draw a diagram.

Answer: _____ Marks: ___ /3

Today's Marks: ___ /6

Day Two Try these.

Today, we will use a bar model to help us visualise each number story.

1 For his birthday, Ollie received €76, which he lodged into his account. He now has €123 in his account. How much did he have before his birthday? 💬

€123

€76	?

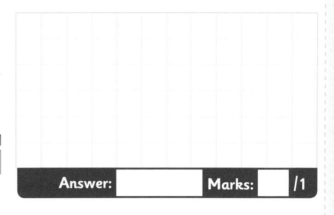
Answer: Marks: /1

2 The bank received 25 cheques on Monday and 40 cheques on Tuesday. How many cheques did it receive in total?

?

25	40

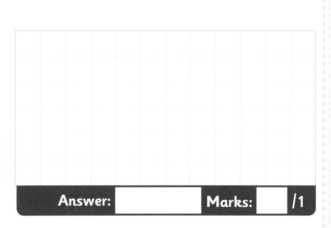
Answer: Marks: /1

3 Callum and Shane own a car dealership. On Saturday, Callum sold 5 cars and Shane sold 3 times that number. How many cars were sold in total?

?

5 cars

5 cars	5 cars	5 cars

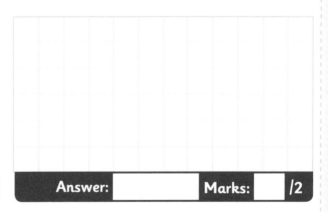
Answer: Marks: /2

4 At the post office, 32 stamps were sold in the morning and 8 were sold in the afternoon. There were 4 assistants working and they each sold an equal amount. How many stamps did each assistant sell?

32 + 8 stamps

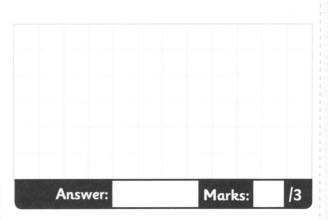
Answer: Marks: /3

Day Three Try these.

Today, we will use a number line to help us visualise each number story.

CLUEs

1. Ethan, Lucas and Mason ordered a different type of pizza each. Ethan ate $\frac{1}{8}$ of his pizza, Lucas ate $\frac{1}{2}$ of his and Mason ate $\frac{1}{4}$ of his. Mark on the number line how much of a pizza each boy ate. Who ate **(a)** the most and **(b)** the least?

Answers: **(a)** _____ **(b)** _____ Marks: [ ] /1

2. Ava started ballet practice at 4:15 pm and it lasted for 40 minutes. At what time was it over?

↓ 4 o'clock   5 o'clock ↓

5   10   15   20   25   30   35   40   45   50   55

Answer: _____ Marks: [ ] /1

3. Oliver finished tennis practice at 5 o'clock. If it lasted for 35 minutes, at what time did it start? (Hint: Count back.)

↓ 4 o'clock   5 o'clock ↓

5   10   15   20   25   30   35   40   45   50   55

Answer: _____ Marks: [ ] /2

4. What was the combined amount of time that Ava and Oliver spent on their hobbies that evening? Use the number lines above to help you.

Answer: _____ Marks: [ ] /3

Today's Marks: [ ] /7

Day Four Try these.

Today, we will use a table to help us visualise each number story.

1. Two girls on an athletics team recorded how long it took them to complete a 100 m sprint. It took girl A 17 seconds and girl B 20 seconds. How long would it take each girl to to complete a 200 m sprint? Fill in the table.

	100 m sprint	200 m sprint
Girl A	17 seconds	
Girl B	20 seconds	

Answer: Marks: /1

2. Evelyn was three days late returning two library books. She owed fines of 20c per day on book A and 40c per day on book B. How much was the total fine on each book by day 3? Fill in the table.

	On day 1	By day 2	By day 3
Book A	20c	40c	
Book B	40c	80c	

Answer: Marks: /2

3. Two boys are saving up their pocket money to buy new runners. Boy A saves €5 per week and boy B saves €10 per week. How much money has each boy saved by week 4? Fill in the table.

	Week 1	By week 2	By week 3	By week 4
Boy A	€5	€10	€15	
Boy B	€10	€20	€30	

Answer: Marks: /3

Today's Marks: /6

Total Marks: /26 | The strategy of visualising helps me to ____

The most important thing I learned was ____

79

19 Division

We are learning to: Share an amount into equal groups. ☐ Divide as repeated subtraction, without and with remainders. ☐ Develop and/or recall division facts within 100. ☐

Day One Study the steps used to solve the problem in the example below.

2 teachers are having a coffee break. They have 8 biscuits to share between them. How many will each get?

Circle the numbers and keywords: 2 teachers, 8 biscuits

Link with operation needed (+, −, × or ÷): **Share** means divide (÷).

Use a strategy: Identify the pattern, 2, 2, 2, 2.

Estimate and calculate:

    My estimate:
    2 groups of 4

    8 ÷ 2 = 4

    Answer: 4

Summarise and check how you got your answer:

    I realised that there was a pattern if 2 people were getting the same number of biscuits and I worked it out.

Try these.

1. Matthew and his grandad went to a fishing shop for some bait. If they bought 30 tubs of bait and plan to go fishing 3 times, how many tubs will they have for each fishing trip? Use repeated subtraction to help you.

   30 − 3 − 3 − 3 − 3 − 3 − 3 − 3 − 3 − 3 − 3 = 1❷

   Answer: 10   **Marks:** /1

2. There are 30 athletes on a running track. The coach splits them up into relay teams of 5. Then, 5 more athletes come to the track. How many athletes will there be on each team now?

   30 − 5 − 5 − 5 − 5 − 5 − 5 = 6 + 5 =

   Answer: **Marks:** /2

3. 50 dogs were entered into a dog show. A further 40 dogs have now been entered online. The dogs will be split up into 10 equal categories. How many dogs will there be in each category?

   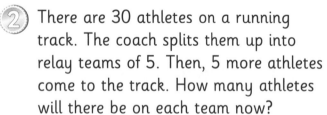

   50 + 40 = 90 − 70 − 10 − 10 − 10 − 10 − 10 − 10 − 10 − 10 = 9

   Answer: 9   **Marks:** /3

Day Two Try these.

1 In the Tropical House at Fota Wildlife Park, there are 28 fish. There are 7 fish in each tank. How many tanks are there?

Top tip:
Identify a pattern.

$$28-7-7-7-7=4$$

Answer: 4   **Marks:** /1

Remember:

groups

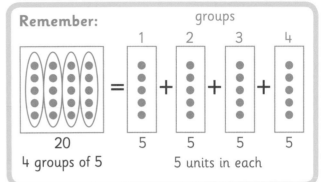

20

4 groups of 5   5 units in each

2 Joe's class are going camping at the Great Outdoors Activity Centre for their school tour. There are 32 boys in the class. If 4 boys can fit in each tent, how many tents will be needed?

$$32- 4-4-4-4-4 4-4-4=8$$

Answer: 8   **Marks:** /1

3 Samantha downloaded 49 songs to her iPod. There were an equal number of songs belonging to each of the following categories: pop, hip hop, rock, jazz, country, R 'n' B and dance. How many songs were there in each category?

$$49-7-7-7-7-7-7-7=7$$

Answer: 7   **Marks:** /2

4 Rhys collects model aeroplanes. He saved up his pocket money and went to a shop to buy more for his collection. The shop had 30 model aeroplanes arranged evenly on 3 shelves. Rhys took 1 from each shelf. How many aeroplanes were left on each shelf then?

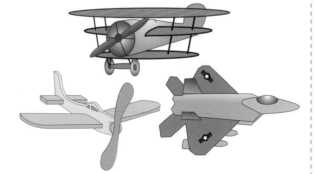

$$30-1-1-1=3$$

Answer: 3   **Marks:** /3

Today's Marks: /7   81

Day Three — Try these.

CLUE's

Divisibility Tips

| **2** Last digit: 2, 4, 6, 8, 0 (even numbers) 24, 72, 106 are multiples of 2 | **3** Digit sum: 3, 6 or 9 51 → 5 + 1 = 6 51 is a multiple of 3 | **5** Last digit: 5 or 0 15, 30, 225 are multiples of 5 | **Digit Sums** Split the number into its digits and add together: 45 → 4 + 5 = 9 |
| **6** Even AND multiple of 3 36 ends in 6 (multiple of 2) 36 → 3 + 6 = 9 (multiple of 3) | **9** Digit sum: 9 72 → 7 + 2 = 9 72 is a multiple of 9 | **10** Last digit: 0 10, 30, 100 are multiples of 10 | You might need to repeat until you get a single-digit answer. 78 → 7 + 8 = 15 15 → 1 + 5 = 6 |

1. Florence the florist has 36 carnations for decorating hairbands to be worn by 4 flower girls at a wedding. If she uses an equal number of carnations for each hairband, how many carnations will there be in each? Will there be any left over?

Answer: _____ Marks: ___ /1

2. On Mother's Day, Florence gets a delivery of 105 fresh tulips. She needs to make 10 bouquets of equal size. How many tulips should she use in each bouquet? Will there be any left over?

Answer: ___ Marks: ___ /1

3. It costs Florence €56 to make 7 sweetheart rose packs for Valentine's Day. If the bow and plastic cost €1 per pack, how much does each rose cost?

Answer: _____ Marks: ___ /2

4. A customer orders a luxury bouquet. Florence uses $\frac{1}{2}$ of the 40 red roses that she has in stock, as well as $\frac{1}{10}$ of the 60 pink roses and $\frac{1}{4}$ of the 20 lilies. How many flowers are in the bouquet in total?

Answer: ___ Marks: ___ /3

Today's Marks: ___ /7

Day Four Try these.

① A fast food van at the Aviva Stadium charges €5 for a hot dog and €3 for a drink. It also has a special offer of a hot dog and a drink for €7. If I have €35, what is the greatest amount of hot dogs and drinks that can I buy?

Top tip: Use trial and improvement.

Answer: **Marks:** /1

② 3rd and 4th Classes go to see a show at the theatre. There are 44 pupils altogether, plus 2 teachers and 2 parents. If there are 8 seats in each row, how many rows will be needed to seat the whole group?

Answer: **Marks:** /2

③ Jamie works at a driving range. At closing time, he gathers up 81 golf balls and sorts them into 9 buckets evenly. He discovers that 1 golf ball in each bucket is damaged. How many good golf balls are in each bucket?

Answer: **Marks:** /3

Today's Marks: /6

Duties

Reader
Calculator
Checker
Reporter

Puzzle power

Complete each division map.

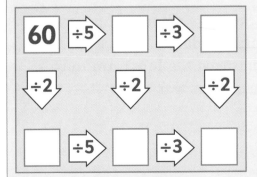

Total Marks: /26 | I am happy with my work solving number stories. Yes ☐ No ☐

I would like to get better at

20 Decimals

We are learning to: Write tenths in decimal form. ☐ Order decimals on a number line. ☐ Understand the value of each digit in a decimal number. ☐

Day One — Study the steps used to solve the problem in the example below.

There are 30 pupils in 3rd Class. 0.1 of them were out sick on Friday. How many pupils were out sick?

CLUES

Keywords

A **decimal fraction** is a number that has a decimal point.

Circle the numbers and keywords: 30 pupils, 0.1 out sick

Link with operation needed (+, −, × or ÷): 0.1 is equivalent to $\frac{1}{10}$. $\frac{1}{10}$ means divide (÷) by 10.

Use a strategy: Visualise, e.g. use a bar model.

Estimate and calculate:
My estimate: less than half the class
$30 ÷ 10 = 3$
Answer: 3 pupils

Summarise and check how you got your answer: I changed 0.1 to $\frac{1}{10}$. To find $\frac{1}{10}$ of 30, I divided 30 by 10.

Try these. **CLUES**

1. Annabel ate 0.4 of her roll at small break. How much of her roll does she have left?

Top tip: Visualise.

Answer: 0.6 — Marks: /1

2. A butcher recieved a supply of ham. He sold 0.3 of it in the morning and 0.4 of it in the afternoon. How much of the ham does he have left to sell?

Answer: 0.3 — Marks: /2

3. Rob, Dan and Amy each get the same amount of pocket money. Their mum told them to save some of it for their holidays. They saved 0.7, 0.5 and 0.3. Rob saved the **greatest** amount and Dan saved the **least amount**. What decimal fraction did they each save?

Answer: Rob: 0.7 Dan: 0.3 — Marks: /3

Day Two Try these.

Fractions and Decimals

| $\frac{0}{10}$ | $\frac{1}{10}$ | $\frac{2}{10}$ | $\frac{3}{10}$ | $\frac{4}{10}$ | $\frac{5}{10}$ | $\frac{6}{10}$ | $\frac{7}{10}$ | $\frac{8}{10}$ | $\frac{9}{10}$ | $\frac{10}{10}$ |

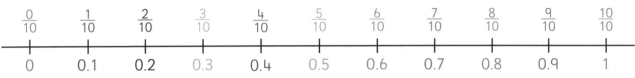

| 0 | 0.1 | 0.2 | 0.3 | 0.4 | 0.5 | 0.6 | 0.7 | 0.8 | 0.9 | 1 |

(1) 100 tickets for a show went on sale online. If 0.5 of them were sold in the first hour, how many tickets was that?

Answer: 50   **Marks:** /1

(2) Wendy was taking part in a sponsored 60 km cycle, but after cycling 0.1 of the distance, her bicycle got a puncture. What distance had she cycled?

Answer: 6 km   **Marks:** /1

(3) Doyle's Sweet Shop has an offer on pick 'n' mix sweets. If you buy 10, you get 0.2 of them free. How many sweets do you pay for?

Joke!

Why did Sally not like decimals?

She didn't see the point!

Answer: 8   **Marks:** /2

(4) The school debate team have completed 0.5 of the debates in a competition. If they have completed 6 debates, how many debates are in the competition altogether?

Answer: 12   **Marks:** /3

Today's Marks: /7

Day Three Try these.

A pet shop received a delivery of 5 different types of snake as follows:

Snake	Length
Corn snake	$1\frac{4}{10}$ m
Milk snake	$1\frac{1}{2}$ m
Python	1.6 m
Rat snake	1.8 m △
King snake	$1\frac{1}{10}$ m △

1. Sam wants a pet snake for his birthday. His mum said that it needs to be as small as possible. Which snake would you advise him to get?

Answer: king snake   **Marks:** /1

2. The pet shop has tanks of different sizes to house the snakes. One of the tanks fits a 1.5 m snake perfectly. Which snake would be best suited to this tank?

Answer: milk snake   **Marks:** /1

3. All of the snakes were measured when they arrived at the pet shop. What was the difference in length between the longest and the shortest?

Answer: 0.7   **Marks:** /2

4. Each snake is fed one mouse per week. If there were 10 mice in storage, what decimal fraction would be needed to feed the snakes for a week?

> **Top tip:**
> Make a table.

Answer: 0.5   **Marks:** /3

Today's Marks: /7

Day Four Try these.

1 10 girls from 3rd Class are on their school's rugby team. 6 of them played in the first match of the season. What decimal fraction of the 3rd Class girls did not play?

Answer: 0. 4   **Marks:** /1

2 Olivia, Lucas and Niall took part in a sponsored run. Olivia ran a distance of 0.9 km and walked the rest of the way. Lucas ran a distance of 0.2 km less than Olivia and Niall ran a distance of 0.1 less than Lucas. What distance did Niall run?

Answer: 0. 6 km   **Marks:** /2

3 A beginners' running club ran distances of 0.4 km on Monday, 0.3 km on Tuesday and $\frac{1}{2}$ km on Wednesday. How many kilometres did they run in total?

Answer: 1. 2 km   **Marks:** /3

Today's Marks: /6

Duties

Reader

Calculator

Checker

Reporter

Super Sleuth investigates

At a talent competition, three judges used score cards to mark the contestants on their performance. Look at the image and answer the questions that follow.

5.5   **10.0**   **4.5**

1. What was the contestant's total score? 20.00

2. Put her marks in order from lowest to highest. 4.5, 5.5, 10.00

3. If she had received 0.2 marks more from each judge, what would her total score have been? 20.6

Total Marks: /26 | **What did I learn in maths this week?**

I would like to get better at

21 Weight

We are learning to: Measure and record weight using appropriate metric units (kg, g). ☐
Add and subtract using units of weight (kg and g). ☐

Day One
Study the steps used to solve the problem in the example below.

Margo bought two 100 g jars of coffee. How much coffee did she buy in total?

CLUES

Keywords

gram (g)

A paperclip weighs about 1 g.

kilogram (kg)

Dictionary

A dictionary weighs about 1 kg.

Circle the numbers and keywords:
two, 100 g jars, how much?

Link with operation needed (+, −, × or ÷):
In total means add (+).

Use a strategy: Identify a pattern.

Estimate and calculate:

	kg	g
My estimate:		100
1 + 1 = 2, so 200	+	100
		200

Answer:
200 g

Summarise and check how you got your answer:
There are 2 jars of coffee with the same amount in each, so there is a double pattern. I added them together.

Try these.

CLUES

1. Zainab has twin baby boys and needs a constant supply of baby formula. She buys two 450 g tins per week. How heavy are they altogether?

Answer: _____   Marks: [ ] /1

2. The Science Discovery Club are making butter. The first group make 220 g, the second group make 245 g and the third group make 210 g. How much butter do they make altogether?

Answer: _____   Marks: [ ] /2

3. The Looney family cleared two loads of rubbish from their garage for recycling. The first load weighed 760 kg and the second load weighed 520 kg. How much rubbish did they recycle altogether?

Answer: _____   Marks: [ ] /3

Strand: Measures Strand Unit: Weight

Today's Marks: [ ] /6

Day Two Try these.

CLUEs

1. A horse and jockey must weigh in before a race. They weigh 511 kg together. If the jockey weighs 57 kg, how heavy is the horse?

Answer: _____ **Marks:** ___ /1

2. Susan wants to send each of her three nephews a parcel in the post. They weigh 185 g, 250 g and 395 g. How much do they weigh altogether?

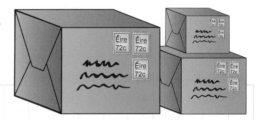

Answer: _____ **Marks:** ___ /1

3. Sandra bought a bag of pick 'n' mix sweets at the cinema. The bag weighed 1,456 g. She gave 360 g to her sister and 435 g to her brother. How much does she have left?

> **Remember:**
> 1 kilogram = 1,000 grams
> 1 kg = 1,000 g

Answer: _____ **Marks:** ___ /2

4. Last week, the Cosy Café got a delivery of napkins weighing 6 kg 560 g. Since then, they have used 4 kg 330 g. What is the weight of the napkins that are left?

> **Top tip:**
> Simplify.

Answer: _____ **Marks:** ___ /3

Day Three Try these.

Chocolate Sponge Ingredients

Ingredient	Quantity for 1 sponge layer	Quantity for 2 sponge layers	Quantity for ☐ sponge layers
Self-raising flour	150 g		
Cocoa	50 g		
Caster sugar	220 g		
Butter	80 g		
Milk	125 ml	250 ml	375 ml
Eggs	2	4	6

Duties

Reader

Calculator

Checker

Reporter

1. Abram's mum is baking him a chocolate sandwich cake with 2 sponge layers for his birthday. Fill in the missing quantities in the third column of the table above.

Answer: _____ Marks: ☐ /1

2. While Abram's mum was measuring out the caster sugar, the bag slipped and 685 g of caster sugar fell into the bowl. How much unwanted sugar was there in the bowl?

Answer: _____ Marks: ☐ /1

3. If Abram asked his mum to add 50 g of chocolate chips to the dry ingredients before adding the butter and eggs, what would the total weight of the dry ingredients (including the chocolate chips) be?

Answer: _____ Marks: ☐ /2

4. If Abram's mum decided to make a jumbo cake with 3 sponge layers, what quantity of each ingredient would she need? Fill in the missing quantities in the fourth column of the table above.

Top tip:
Visualise.

Answer: _____ Marks: ☐ /3

Today's Marks: ☐ /7

Day Four Try these.

1. 100 g of milk chocolate contains 30 g of fat. How much fat is there a large bar of milk chocolate weighing 500 g?

Top tip: Make a table.

Answer: | Marks: | /1

2. Donal ate 37 g of cereal for breakfast, 48 g of bread for lunch and 54 g of pasta for dinner. How many grams of carbohydrates did he eat altogether?

Answer: | Marks: | /2

3. 3rd Class were eating healthily for Active Week in school. The local greengrocers supplied them with fresh fruit for lunch and the pupils weighed the fruit before they ate it. They ate 1,750 g of fruit on Monday, 1,890 g on Tuesday and 2,010 g on Wednesday. How many grams of fruit had the pupils eaten by home time on Wednesday?

Answer: | Marks: | /3

Today's Marks: | /6

Duties

Reader

Calculator

Checker

Reporter

Super Sleuth investigates

1. How does a butcher measure the meat that is sold?

2. Would you buy 1 gram or 1 kilogram of meat?

3. Can you write your own questions based on weight?

Total Marks: | /26 | I enjoyed this unit, because

The most important thing I learned was

22  Sequences and Number Sentences

We are learning to: Identify and continue repeating patterns. ☐ Use patterns as an aid to remember facts. ☐ Identify the rules of sequences and continue them. ☐ Change a number sentence to a word problem. ☐

Day One Study the steps used to solve the problem in the example below.

What comes next in this sequence? What is the rule?

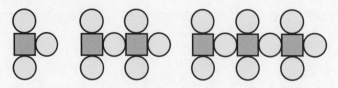

CLUES

Circle the numbers and keywords:

next, sequence, rule

Link with operation needed (+, −, × or ÷): None

Use a strategy: Make a table.

Item	1st term	2nd term	3rd term	4th term	Rule
Square	1	2	3	?	+1 square
Circle	3	6	9	?	+3 circles

Estimate and calculate:

My estimate: add
1 square, add 3 circles

$3 + 1 = 4$ squares
$9 + 3 = 12$ circles

Answer:
4 squares,
12 circles

Summarise and check how you got your answer:
I found the rule for each shape and followed the sequence.

Try these.

CLUES

Item	1st term	2nd term	3rd term	4th term	5th term
Blue hexagon	2	3	4		
Pink hexagon	2	4	6		

① Look at the sequence above. What is the rule?

Answer: _____ Marks: ☐ /1

② Write the fourth term in the table. Marks: ☐ /2

③ Write the fifth term in the table. Marks: ☐ /3

Strand: **Algebra** Strand Unit: Number Patterns and Sequences; Number Sentences

Today's Marks: ☐ /6

Day Two Try these.

1 Mark at the local filling station likes to stack the take-away cups tidily every morning. He places 3 cups in the first stack, 6 in the second stack and 9 in the third stack. If the pattern continues, how many cups will he place in the fourth stack?

Answer: | Marks: | /1

2 At a local garden centre, a gardener is planting trays of seeds. She plants 2 seeds in the first tray, 4 seeds in the second tray and 8 seeds in the third tray. How many seeds will she plant in the fourth tray if the pattern continues?

Answer: | Marks: | /1

3 Lexie is training for a marathon by running laps on a running track daily. On Monday, she runs 5 laps, on Tuesday, she runs 11 laps and on Wednesday, she runs 18 laps. How many laps do you anticipate her running on Thursday?

Answer: | Marks: | /2

4 Molly is making ice-cream sundaes for dessert for herself and her family. If she puts 2 mini marshmallows on her baby brother's sundae, 12 on her own and 22 on her mum's, how many do you think she will put on her dad's?

Top tip: Make a table.

Answer: | Marks: | /3

Day Three Try these.

1. Mr Humphreys uses his greenhouse for growing vegetables. He likes to plant them in rows and create sequences with different types. If he has 6 rows of lettuce, 8 rows of peas and 11 rows of tomatoes, how many rows of onions do you think he has?

Answer: _____ Marks: ____ /1

2. Mr Humphreys has a plentiful supply of cucumbers growing in his greenhouse. On the first plant there are 4, on the second there are 8, on the third there are 16 and on the fourth there are 32. How many should be on the fifth plant if they are growing in sequence?

Answer: _____ Marks: ____ /1

3. Mr Humphreys has planted a grapevine and it is growing at a rate of 5 cm per week. If it is 10 cm tall at the end of the second week, what height will it be at the end of the sixth week?

Answer: _____ Marks: ____ /2

4. Mr Humphrey's strawberries are beginning to ripen. On the first day, he has 1 ripe strawberry. On the second day, he has 4. On the third day, he has 9. On the fourth day, he has 16. What is the next number in the sequence likely to be?

Top tip:
Identify a pattern.

Answer: _____ Marks: ____ /3

Super Sleuth challenge

Take any three numbers in a sequence. Multiply the middle number by itself. Next, multiply the first number by the third number. Try this a few times with different sequences. What do the answers have in common? Are there any numbers that do not fit?

Today's Marks: ____ /7

Day Four Try these.

1. Carla's dad gets his car washed weekly at the local filling station. If the car wash costs €10, how much does he spend in a month?

> **Top tip:** Identify a pattern.

Answer: _____ **Marks:** ___ /1

2. The Pierce family bought a new flatscreen TV. On the first day, the children spent 80 minutes watching cartoons, but their mum said that was far too long. She told them to halve the time they spend watching cartoons each day thereafter. How long did they spend watching TV on the third day?

Answer: _____ **Marks:** ___ /2

3. Jamal went to Disneyland Paris for three days. He went on 6 rides the first day, 12 the second day and 24 the third day. How many rides did he go on altogether? Can you identify the sequence?

Answer: _____ **Marks:** ___ /3

Today's Marks: ___ /6

Super Sleuth challenge

In your copy, write a number story to go with the following number sentence:

14 + ☐ = 30

Duties

Reader

Calculator

Checker

Reporter

Super Sleuth investigates

1. What pattern is made by the piano keys?

2. How many piano keys do you think there are?

3. Can you think of any maths questions based on the image?

Total Marks: ___ /26 | I am happy with my work solving number stories. Yes ☐ No ☐

One thing that helped me was _____

23 🔍 Revision 4

Day One The Cruise Ship

Try these.

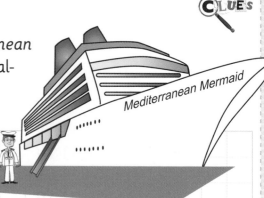

Mediterranean Mermaid

1. The captain and 24 deck officers of the *Mediterranean Mermaid* share living quarters. If they have 5 equal-sized compartments between them, how many stay in each compartment?

Answer: _____ Marks: _____ /1

2. There are 28 lifeguards on duty at the 4 swimming pools on the ship. How many lifeguards are on duty at each pool?

Answer: _____ Marks: _____ /1

3. The job of carrying 18 suitcases for passengers was shared equally between 6 porters. How many suitcases did each porter carry?

Answer: _____ Marks: _____ /2

4. At the ship's cinema, 40 films were shown during a 10-day cruise, with an equal number of films shown each day. How many films were shown each day? 💬

Answer: _____ Marks: _____ /3

Strand: **Number** Strand Units: Operations – division; Decimals
Strand: **Measures** Strand Unit: Weight
Strand: **Algebra** Strand Units: Number Patterns and Sequences; Number Sentences

Today's Marks: _____ /7

Day Two Try these.

1 Marian and Paul went on a 10-day cruise to celebrate their golden wedding anniversary. If they have already completed 0.3 of the cruise, how much of the cruise is still left?

Answer: _____ Marks: ___ /1

2 Only 0.8 of 100 passengers turned up at the safety demonstration for their deck. How many passengers attended the demonstration?

Answer: _____ Marks: ___ /1

3 On the first night of the cruise, Chloe ate 0.6 of her dessert and gave 0.2 to one of her friends for a taster. How much of the dessert was left over?

Answer: _____ Marks: ___ /2

4 A group of friends saved 0.1 of the cost of the cruise by booking their tickets together and qualifying for a group discount. If the full price of a ticket was €600, how much did each person pay after the discount was subtracted from their ticket?

Answer: _____ Marks: ___ /3

Today's Marks: ___ /7

Day Three Try these.

CLUEs

1 The ship's pantry was stocked with 9,000 g of butter for the cruise. If 3,500 g of butter was used in the first half of the cruise, how much was left for the remainder of the cruise?

Answer: _____ Marks: ____ /1

2 A 500 g box of chocolates was given to each passenger on arrival. If a family of 4 received a box each, what weight of chocolate did they receive in total?

Answer: _____ Marks: ____ /1

3 93 kg of minced beef, 388 kg of roast beef and 424 kg of beefsteak were cooked on the ship each day. How much beef was cooked each day in total?

Answer: _____ Marks: ____ /2

4 Donna packed a vanity case of toiletries weighing 12 kg and a suitcase of clothing and shoes weighing 30 kg. If each of her 4 friends had done likewise, what was the combined weight of the group's luggage?

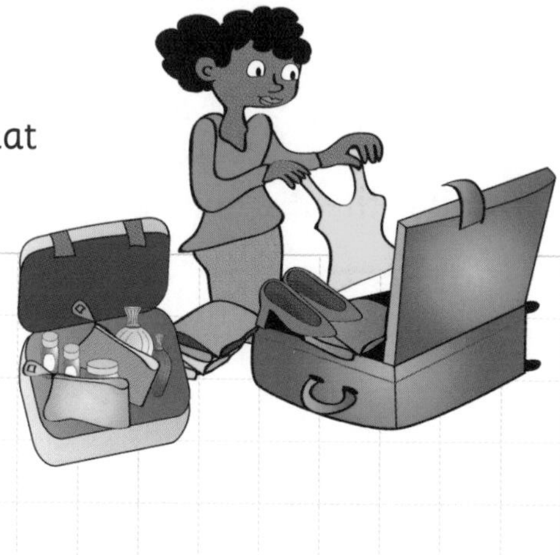

Answer: _____ Marks: ____ /3

Today's Marks: ____ /7

Day Four — Try these.

1. Write a number sentence for the following number story:
87 passengers are on deck watching a fireworks display on the last night of the cruise. 45 more passengers arrive on deck and 25 passengers leave to escape the cold. How many passengers are left on deck?

Mediterranean Mermaid

Answer: _____ Marks: ___ /1

2. Write a number story based on a cruise ship for the following number sentence:

150 g – 76 g =

Answer: _____
_____
_____

Marks: ___ /2

3. The *Mediterranean Mermaid* has 4 anchors weighing 225 kg each. How heavy are the anchors in total?

Answer: _____ Marks: ___ /3

Today's Marks: ___ /6

Duties

Reader
Calculator
Checker
Reporter

Super Sleuth investigates

1. How many windows do you think are on this cruise ship?

2. If you were piloting the ship, how fast would it go?

3. Can you think of any maths questions based on the image?

24 Strategy: Act it Out

Day One

The act-it-out strategy encourages you to think creatively by using concrete materials to break down a number story. This might involve using blocks, teddy bears, unifix cubes, counters, lollipop sticks or money to act out the story, making it easier for you to understand. This strategy can be fun if you like to be active while you work!

Today, we will use counters to help us break down each number story.

Try these.

1 3rd Class are going zip lining on their school tour. The park's policy is that 1 adult must accompany every 4 children who attend. If 36 children are going on the tour, how many adults must also attend? Use counters to help you.

Answer: _____ Marks: ____ /1

2 On the zip lining course, for every 3 lines that you complete, you get a treasure-hunt clue. If there are 15 lines to complete, how many clues are there to collect? Use counters to help you.

Answer: _____ Marks: ____ /1

3 36 children in 3rd Class are split up into 8 teams. If 4 children from another school join them in order to make equal-sized teams, how many children are there on each team? Use counters to help you.

Answer: _____ Marks: ____ /2

4 At closing time, the instructors have to put away the safety harnesses. If one group used 36, another group used 26 and there were 15 spares, how many safety harnesses were there in total? Use counters to help you.

Answer: _____ Marks: ____ /3

Today's Marks: ____ /7

Day Two Try these.

1. At a school cake sale, fairy cakes cost 50c each.
If Amy has €2.50, how many fairy cakes can she buy?
Use money to help you.

Answer: | Marks: | /1

2. Maeve wants to divide €20.00 from her change jar equally between her 5 grandchildren. What is the least amount of coins that each child will receive? Use money to help you.

Answer: | Marks: | /1

3. On Saturday, a busker was given 4 €5 notes, 5 €2 coins and 15 €1 coins. How much money was he given in total? Use money to help you.

Answer: | Marks: | /2

4. Dylan was buying new socks and underwear for his holidays. He gave the shopkeeper a €20 note, a €10 note and a €5 note. How much did they cost if he got €2.35 change? Use money to help you.

Answer: | Marks: | /3

Today's Marks: | /7

Day Three Try these.

Today, we will act it out to help us break down each number story.

 CLUEs

1. A spider begins crawling up a wall. He crawls foward 5 cm, drops back 2 cm, crawls foward 6 cm and drops back 1 cm. How many centimetres up the wall has he moved? Act it out.

Answer: _____ Marks: ____ /1

2. There is a 750 ml jug of cordial on the table. Abbey comes home thirsty and fills a glass with 250 ml of cordial. Her brother Stephen comes along and adds 100 ml of water to the jug, because he thinks the cordial is too strong. How much cordial is in the jug now? Act it out.

Answer: _____ Marks: ____ /1

3. A window cleaner is standing on the middle rung of a ladder and cleaning the windows of an office building. He climbs up 3 rungs, but notices that he has missed a spot below and climbs down 7 rungs. He has to climb up 10 rungs to reach the top of the ladder. How many rungs are there? Act out the positions.

Answer: _____ Marks: ____ /2

4. There are 29 pupils in a line for PE. The teacher picks the first pupil for an actvity and then every fourth pupil after that. How many pupils does the teacher pick? Act it out or use lollipop sticks as people.

Answer: _____ Marks: ____ /3

Today's Marks: ____ /7

Day Four Try these.

Today, we will act it out to help us break down each number story.

CLUEs

1. Arrange 14 blocks into three groups. The third group should have 1 more than the first and twice as many as the second. How many blocks are there in each group? Act it out.

Answer: _____ Marks: ☐ /1

2. The local football club are holding a competition to design a new flag for the club. The club's colours are red, yellow and black. Based on the template shown, how many different ways can you colour the flag? Act it out.

Marks: ☐ /2

3. Choose 9 pupils from the class and give each a number between 1 and 9 written on a piece of paper. These 9 pupils must now form groups of 3 so that the digits in each group add up to 15. Act it out.

1	2	3
4	5	6
7	8	9

Marks: ☐ /3

Today's Marks: ☐ /6

Total Marks: ☐ /27 | The activities were fun, because _____

I could now teach a friend how to _____

25 Symmetry

We are learning to: Identify symmetry in the environment. ☐
Identify and draw lines of symmetry in two-dimensional shapes. ☐

Day One
Study the steps used to solve the problem in the example below.

In a deck of cards, there are 4 suits: spades, hearts, diamonds and clubs. Which suit symbol has horizontal symmetry?

Clues

Circle the numbers and keywords: symbol, horizontal symmetry

Link with operation needed (+, −, × or ÷): None

Use a strategy: Act it out.

Estimate and calculate:

My estimate: diamond **Answer:** diamond

Keywords

A **symmetrical** object has 2 identical parts facing each other.

Summarise and check how you got your answer:
I knew that all of the symbols had symmetry, but I had to investigate which had vertical or horizontal symmetry. I used my ruler to help me.

Try these.

Clues

(1) 4 butterflies have hatched from their cocoons. How many lines of symmetry are there?

Marks: ___ /1

(2) How many lines of symmetry are in 6 starfish like the one shown?

Answer: ___ Marks: ___ /2

(3) There are 20 lines of symmetry in 4 car wheels like the one shown. How many lines of symmetry are there in 5 of these car wheels?

Answer: ___ Marks: ___ /3

Strand: Shape and Space Strand Unit: Symmetry

Today's Marks: ___ /6

Day Two Try these.

A W L D X H I M V O T

 ① All of the letters above are symmetrical. Can you identify how many lines of symmetry there are in the name TOM?

Top tip: Act it out.

Answer: ⬛ Marks: ⬛ /1

② Which of the letters above are also symmetrical in their lower-case form?

Answer: ⬛ Marks: ⬛ /1

 ③ What other capital letters (not shown above) are symmetrical? Demonstrate your answer.

Marks: ⬛ /2

 ④ Symmetry can be explained in several ways, such as:

- Horizontal line symmetry, e.g. ~~COB~~
- Vertical line symmetry, e.g. T◊T
- Mirror symmetry
- Words that can be read upside down, e.g. SOS
- Palindrome, e.g. RADAR

Can you think of your own ways to explain symmetry using letters?

Top tip: Symmetry is found in nature, in shapes and also in buildings. Look closely at the image of the Taj Mahal. Can you find the line of symmetry?

Answer: _____

_____

Marks: ⬛ /3

Today's Marks: ⬛ /7   **105**

Day Three Try these.

CLUEs

1 How many many lines of symmetry are there in 6 square tiles?

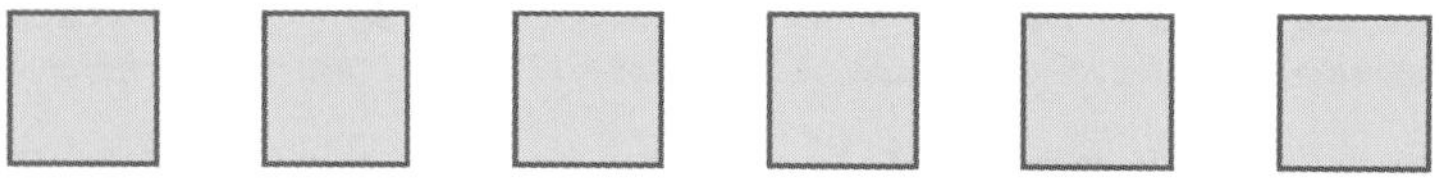

Top tip:
Identify a pattern.

Answer: _____ Marks: ___ /1

2 There are 9 snooker tables in a snooker hall. Each table has a triangle for arranging the red balls. How many lines of symmetry are there in the 9 triangles?

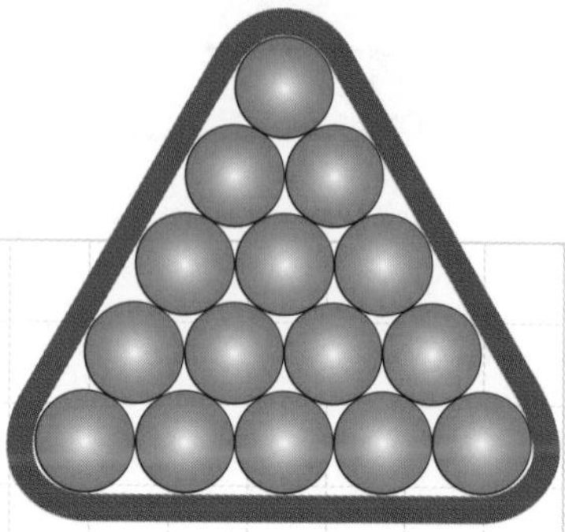

Answer: _____ Marks: ___ /1

3 Alma is crocheting a baby blanket for her newborn grandson. The blanket will have a design of hexagons. It will have 4 yellow hexagons and 10 blue hexagons. How many lines of symmetry will there be in all of the hexagons?

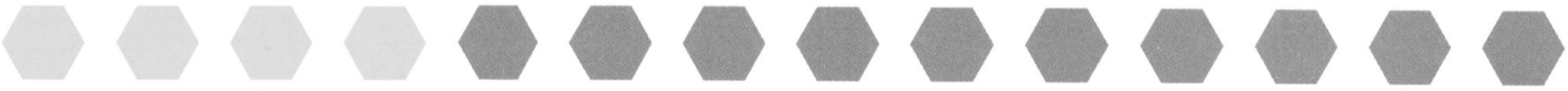

Answer: _____ Marks: ___ /2

4 There are 8 diamond-shaped kites in a seaside shop. These have 16 lines of symmetry in total. If the shopkeeper sells two kites, how many lines of symmetry will be left?

Answer: _____ Marks: ___ /3

Today's Marks: ___ /7

Day Four Try these.

Top tip: Visualise.

 1 The O'Sullivan brothers are famous for their award-winning symmetrical building projects. Archie is an architect, while Des is an interior designer. Look at the image. Can you help Archie to complete the design for this house so that it is symmetrical?

Marks: ☐ /1

 2 Des is working on a bedroom design for twin boys whose ninth birthday is fast approaching. Can you help Des to complete the design so that it is symmetrical?

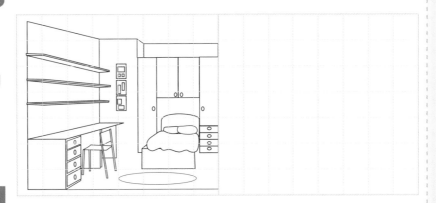

Marks: ☐ /2

 3 Look at the floor plan below. Design your own symmetrical floor plan for a bungalow.

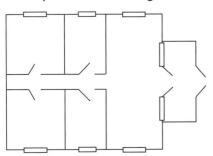

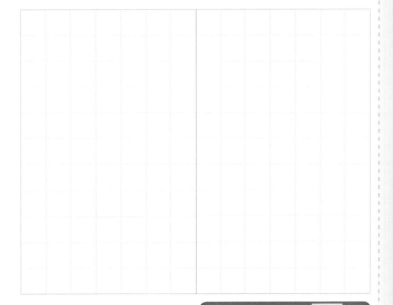

Marks: ☐ /3

Today's Marks: ☐ /6

Maths art 💬
With your partner, print out a photograph of yourself, cut it in half and glue one half to a sheet of paper. Draw your missing side. (You could also use photographs of celebrities from magazines.)

Total Marks: ☐ /26 | If I worked with a partner, I helped by ☐

My favourite activity was ☐

26 Area

We are learning to: Estimate and measure area. ☐ Measure the area of irregular and regular shapes. ☐
Measure area in square units. ☐

Day One Study the steps used to solve the problem in the example below.

What is the area of this shape?

CLUES

Keywords

Area is the amount of space taken up by a surface. We measure area in squares.

Circle the numbers and keywords: area, shape

Link with operation needed (+, −, × or ÷): None

Use a strategy: Visualise.

Estimate and calculate:

My estimate: $2 \times 3 = 6$	Count the squares.	**Answer:** 6 square units

Summarise and check how you got your answer:
I counted the number of coloured squares.

Try these.

CLUES

Swimming Pool A (pool = shaded area)

Swimming Pool B (pool = shaded area)

① What is the combined area of both pools?

| Answer: | Marks: | /1 |

② What is the difference between the two areas?

| Answer: | Marks: | /2 |

③ What is the combined area of the white viewing zone at both pools?

| Answer: | Marks: | /3 |

Today's Marks: /6

Day Two Try these.

1 A football pitch is being reseeded for the coming season. Calculate the area of the football pitch being reseeded (shaded area).

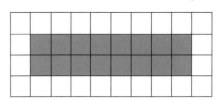

Answer: | **Marks:** | /1

2 A new car park is being built. Each car space takes up 2 purple square units. How many car spaces would 40 purple square units provide?

Answer: | **Marks:** | /1

3 Tony vacuums 6 classrooms each day after school. If 3 of the classrooms are the same size as classroom A and the other 3 are the same size as classroom B, how many square units does Tony vacuum each day?

Classroom A   Classroom B

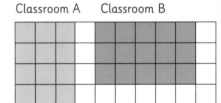

Answer: | **Marks:** | /2

4 Susan buys a roll of frosted film to cover the windows of the two bathrooms in her office. The area of each pane of glass is shaded pink in the diagram. If there are 4 panes of glass in bathroom A and 6 panes of glass in bathroom B, how many square units are there altogether?

Answer: | **Marks:** | /3

Super Sleuth challenge

Write a number sentence for the total area of the diagram, thinking of it as one rectangle or two.

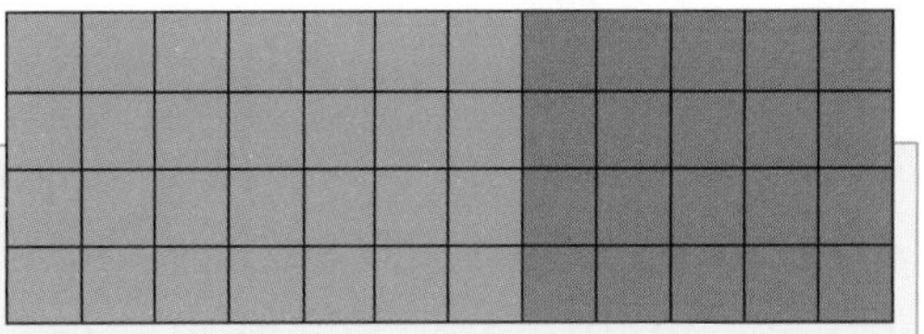

     × (+   ) =   ×   +   ×   =

Day Three Try these.

1 3rd Class are learning to sew using binca and wool. Estimate and then measure the area of Harry's pattern shown.

Top tip: Identify a pattern.

Answer: _____ **Marks:** ___ /1

2 If Sam makes 2 heart patterns for his mum to sew onto a cushion cover, how many red square units will there be altogether?

Answer: _____ **Marks:** ___ /1

3 Matilda is designing flowers for her pillowcase. She uses 256 square units in total. How many flowers will she make?

Answer: _____ **Marks:** ___ /2

4 Chloe is creating a pattern of butterflies. She wants 1 entire butterfly and 2 butterflies with only one wing each, so that they look as if they are folding their wings. There are 48 square units in an entire butterfly. How many square units will she use altogether?

Answer: _____ **Marks:** ___ /3

Super Sleuth challenge

With your partner, design your own patterns. One should have 20 square units and the other should have 50 square units.

Today's Marks: ___ /7

Day Four Try these.

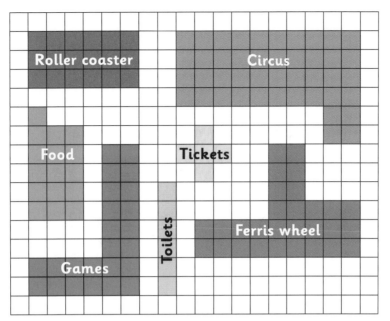

1 Look at the plan of a carnival above. What area does the Ferris wheel take up?

Answer: _____ Marks: ____ /1

2 The ticket stand at the carnival is in the middle of the grounds. If it was twice as big as it is now, how many square units would it take up?

Answer: _____ Marks: ____ /2

3 If an additional toilet block of 6 square units was needed on the carnival grounds, where could you build it? Draw it on the plan.

Marks: ____ /3

Today's Marks: ____ /6

Puzzle power

Duties

Reader
Calculator
Checker
Reporter

How many squares are in this image? Be careful; some squares are hidden!

Total Marks: ____ /26 | I still have a question about _____

I could now teach a friend how to _____

111

27 3-D Shapes

We are learning to: Identify, describe and compare 3-D shapes. ☐ Describe the relationship of 3-D shapes with constituent 2-D shapes. ☐ Identify nets. ☐ Solve and complete practical tasks and problems involving 3-D shapes. ☐ Identify the use of 3-D shapes in the environment. ☐

Day One Study the steps used to solve the problem in the example below.

There are 6 faces on a cube. How many faces are there on 2 cubes?

CLUES

Circle the numbers and keywords: 6, 2, faces, cube

Link with operation needed (+, −, × or ÷): Add (+).

Use a strategy: Make a model.

Estimate and calculate:

My estimate:
double the number 6

$6 + 6 = 12$ **Answer:** 12

Summarise and check how you got your answer:
6 faces on 1 cube, 12 faces on 2 cubes.

Keywords

A **face** is a surface on a 3-D shape. The base of a 3-D shape is also a face.

Try these.

1 How many circular bases are there in total on 5 cylinders and 7 cones?

$5 + 5 × 7 ±$

Answer: 17   **Marks:** /1

2 20 cuboid boxes were used to create a stage set for a concert. If 2 of the boxes were removed by a stagehand, how many faces were there on the boxes that were left on stage?

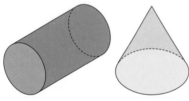

$\begin{array}{r} 18 \\ \times\ 6 \\ {\scriptstyle 4} \\ \hline 108 \end{array}$

Answer: 108   **Marks:** /2

3 Liz has 10 Toblerones in one bag and 4 square-based pyramid boxes of Ferrero Rocher in another bag. How many more boxes of Ferrero Rocher are needed for each bag to contain an equal number of triangular faces?

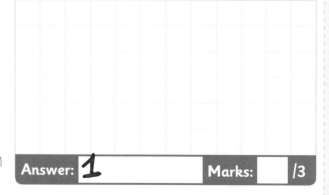

Answer: 1   **Marks:** /3

Today's Marks: /6

Day Two Try these.

CLUES

1 Finn's mum buys new storage boxes for the playroom. They come in cubes and cuboids, so she buys 2 of each. How many edges are there altogether on the 4 boxes?

Keywords

An **edge** is where two faces meet on a 3-D shape.

Answer: 24   Marks: /1

2 The O'Mearas are going camping for the weekend. They bring 3 tents with them: one for the parents, one for the children and one to store their belongings. How many edges are there in total on the 3 tents?

Answer: 27   Marks: /1

3 In a newly built estate, the roofs of the houses are constructed in the shape of a square-based pyramid. If there are 40 edges on the roofs in total, how many houses are there in the estate?

Answer: 5   Marks: /2

4 An ice-cream van calls to a school at the end of the year to give the pupils in the best classes an ice-cream cone as an award. If 21 pupils from 5th Class, 24 pupils from 4th Class and 22 pupils from 3rd Class each get an ice-cream cone, how many curved edges are there in total on the cones?

Answer: 134   Marks: /3

Today's Marks: /7   113

Day Three Try these.

There is a tower-building competition taking place at school. Using the shapes below and the number of **vertices** given for each, identify which shapes would be the most suitable for building a tower. Answer the questions that follow.

Cube (8) Triangular prism (6) Cone (1) Cuboid (8) Cylinder (0) Sphere (0) Square-based pyramid (5)

Keywords

Vertex (plural: **vertices**) means corner. The edges of a 3-D shape meet at a vertex.

Top tip:
Make a model.

1. According to the rules of the competition, the first tower built must have at least 22 vertices (corners). Which shapes are needed to build a tower with at least 22 vertices? Draw your tower.

Answer: _triangular prism cube and cuboid_   Marks: ___ /1

2. The second tower built must have at least 33 vertices. Which shapes are needed to build a tower with at least 33 vertices? Draw your tower.

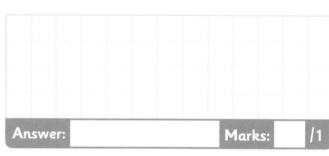

Answer: _____   Marks: ___ /1

3. The third tower must be built using 2 cylinders, 1 cuboid and 1 triangular prism. How many vertices would there be in this tower in total?

Answer: _____   Marks: ___ /2

4. Which of these towers has the greatest number of vertices?

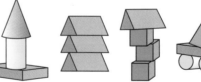

Answer: _____   Marks: ___ /3

Today's Marks: ___ /7

Day Four Try these.

Top tip: Use trial and improvement.

CLUEs

	A	B
3		
2		
1		

Solve the clues below in order to fill in the grid.

1 Write the names of the shapes in the grid above: The shape at A3 has one curved edge and two faces. The shape at A1 has 6 square faces.

Marks: /1

2 The shape at B3 has two triangular faces and three rectangular faces. The cuboid is between the cylinder and the triangular prism.

Marks: /2

3 The shape that is between the cone and the cube has no vertices.

Marks: /3

Today's Marks: /6

Duties

Reader

Calculator

Checker

Reporter

Super Sleuth investigates

1. Where was the photograph taken?

2. Do you recognise the 3-D shapes?

3. How many of these shapes are there?

4. Can you think of any maths questions based on the image?

Total Marks: /26 | My favourite activity was

I could use what I've learned when

115

28 Capacity

We are learning to: Measure capacity in litres and millilitres. ☐ Add and subtract litres and millilitres. ☐

Day One — Study the steps used to solve the problem in the example below.

Jim bought a tin of paint containing 4 litres (l) to paint the interior of a restaurant. If he used 2,560 ml of paint to complete the job, how much was left?

CLUEs

Keywords

A **millilitre (1 ml)** is a tiny amount of liquid. A teaspoon holds about 5 ml.

Circle the numbers and keywords:
4 litres, paint, used 2,560 ml, how much was left?

Link with operation needed (+, −, × or ÷):
How much was left? means take away (−).

Use a strategy: Visualise.

Estimate and calculate:

My estimate: around 2,000 ml

l	ml
4	000
− 2	560
1	440

Answer: 1,440 ml

Summarise and check how you got your answer:
Jim had 4 litres of paint and used 2,560 ml, so it was removed from the tin and there was an amount left.

Try these.

CLUEs

1. At the filling station, two drivers are buying petrol. One buys 57 litres and the other buys 65 litres. How many litres do they buy altogether?

    Answer: _____ Marks: ___ /1

2. Jessica has a cold, so her mum gives her a hot lemon drink twice a day. If the hot lemon drink fills a 275 ml beaker, how much does she take in a day?

    Answer: _____ Marks: ___ /2

3. On a hot summer day, Mr Walsh fills a large paddling pool in the back garden for his children. He also fills a small paddling pool for their dog to help him keep cool. It takes 2 l 300 ml of water to fill the large pool and 1 l 740 ml to fill the small pool. How much water is used in total?

    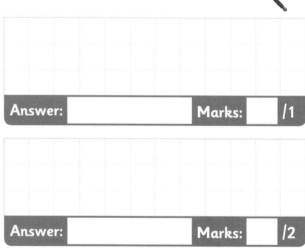

    Answer: _____ Marks: ___ /3

Today's Marks: ___ /6

Day Two Try these.

 CLUEs

1. Jack polishes cars at a garage. In the morning, he takes a full bottle of polish containing 873 ml from the storeroom. By lunchtime, he has used 495 ml. How much polish is left?

Answer: Marks: /1

2. A bath uses up 85 litres of water, while a power shower uses up 134 litres for an 8-minute shower. How much water will Mrs Luttrell save by taking a bath?

Answer: Marks: /1

3. You can't spell 'teacher' without 'tea'! Teachers love their tea and vast amounts of it are made in the staffroom. If Ms Lyton makes a 500 ml pot of tea and uses this to fill a 145 ml cup for herself and a 243 ml mug for Ms Manning, how much tea is left in the pot for Ms Parker?

Answer: Marks: /2

4. Tom, Mattock and Dylan buy water balloons at the shop. They each fill 2 balloons with 354 ml of water. They throw 2 balloons at Joe and 1 at Karl. How many millilitres of water are left in the unburst balloon?

Top tip: Identify a pattern.

Answer: Marks: /3

Today's Marks: /7

Day Three Try these.

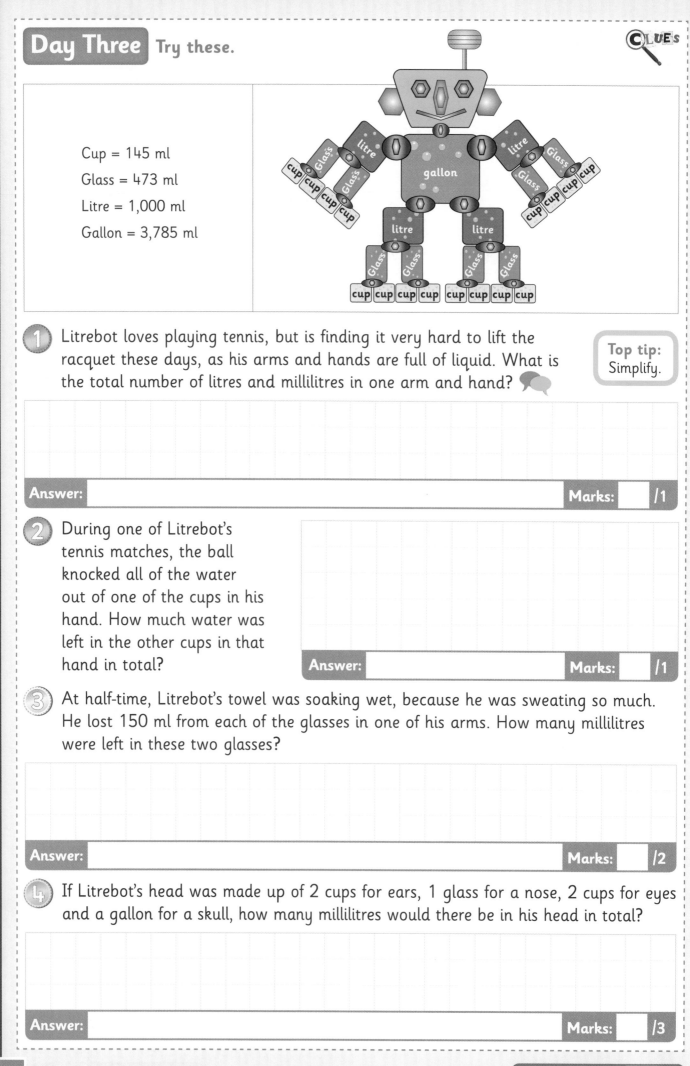

Cup = 145 ml

Glass = 473 ml

Litre = 1,000 ml

Gallon = 3,785 ml

Clues

1. Litrebot loves playing tennis, but is finding it very hard to lift the racquet these days, as his arms and hands are full of liquid. What is the total number of litres and millilitres in one arm and hand?

Top tip: Simplify.

Answer: ⬚ Marks: ⬚ /1

2. During one of Litrebot's tennis matches, the ball knocked all of the water out of one of the cups in his hand. How much water was left in the other cups in that hand in total?

Answer: ⬚ Marks: ⬚ /1

3. At half-time, Litrebot's towel was soaking wet, because he was sweating so much. He lost 150 ml from each of the glasses in one of his arms. How many millilitres were left in these two glasses?

Answer: ⬚ Marks: ⬚ /2

4. If Litrebot's head was made up of 2 cups for ears, 1 glass for a nose, 2 cups for eyes and a gallon for a skull, how many millilitres would there be in his head in total?

Answer: ⬚ Marks: ⬚ /3

Today's Marks: ⬚ /7

Day Four Try these.

 1 Bob and Conor both drive a lorry for a living. Bob's lorry's consumption of diesel in a day is 4,325 ml and Conor's is 5,436 ml. What is the difference in millilitres?

Answer: _____ **Marks:** [ ] /1

2 A milkman delivered 46 l 100 ml of full-fat milk and 51 l 195 ml of low-fat milk to his customers. He later discovered that 1,450 ml of milk was sour. How many litres of milk were fresh?

Answer: _____ **Marks:** [ ] /2

3 Carly has two pet fish called Fred and Wilma. Her fish tank holds 7 l 570 ml of water. While cleaning the tank, she removes half of the water, leaving 3,785 ml. She then adds 1,345 ml to the tank. How much more water must she add for the tank to be full?

Answer: _____ **Marks:** [ ] /3

Today's Marks: [ ] /6

Duties

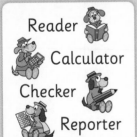

Reader

Calculator

Checker

Reporter

Super Sleuth investigates

1. How many litres of water do you think the water cooler holds?

2. If a cup holds 75 ml, how many cups do you think the workers drink in a day?

3. Can you think of any maths questions based on the image?

Total Marks: [ ] /26 | **In this unit, I liked** _____

I understand more about _____

29 🔍 Revision 5

Day One Hollywood

Try these.

1 Which letters in the 'HOLLYWOOD' sign are symmetrical? Explain your reasoning. 💬

Answer: _____ Marks: ☐ /1

2 A symmetrical smile is said to be a 'Hollywood smile'. Can you identify symmetry in the image?

Answer: _____ Marks: ☐ /1

3 At the Hollywood Walk of Fame, stars are placed on the ground containing the names of famous people. How many lines of symmetry are there in 5 stars?

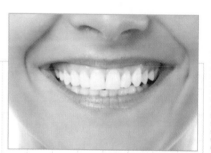

Answer: _____ Marks: ☐ /2

4 Disney's Hollywood Studios are a popular destination for tourists. The Mickey Mouse ears are symmetrical. If 4 souvenir shops at the studios each sell 10 Mickey Mouse hats, how many lines of symmetry is that? 💬

Answer: _____ Marks: ☐ /3

Strand: Shape and Space Strand Units: Symmetry; 3-D Shapes
Strand: Measures Strand Units: Area; Capacity

Today's Marks: ☐ /7

Day Two Try these.

CLUEs

1. The area of the lake on the grounds of Disney's Hollywood Studios is shown in the diagram. Approximately how many square units does it cover?

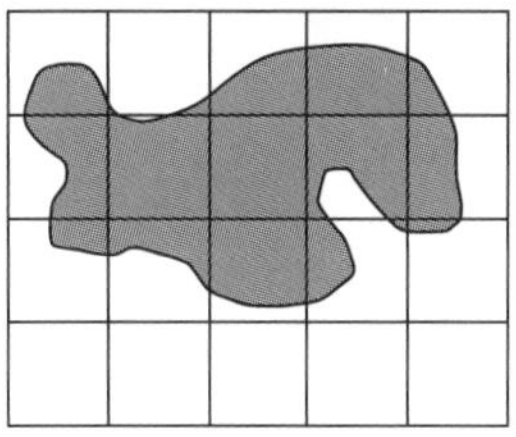

Answer: Marks: /1

2. A sign stands at the entrance to the grounds. How many square units does it cover?

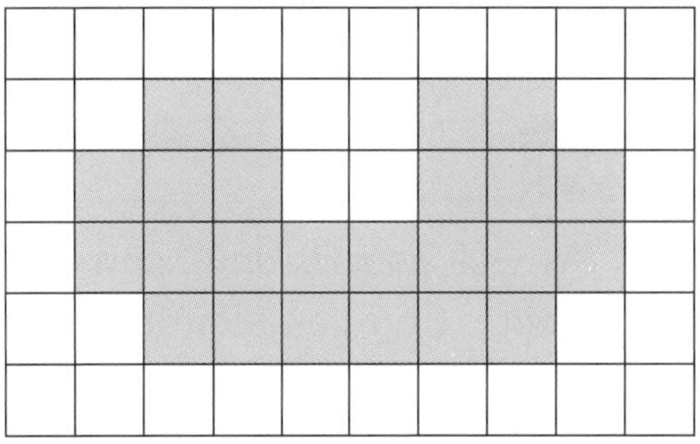

Answer: Marks: /1

3. There are two equal-sized towers on the grounds. The diagram shows the base of one tower. Approximately how many square units do they both cover?

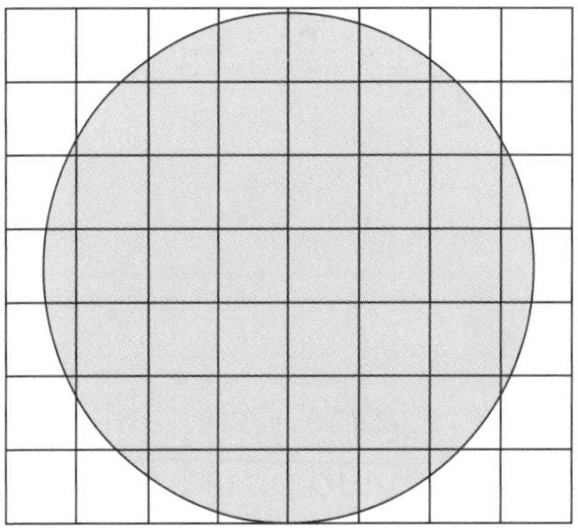

Answer: Marks: /2

4. If one of the studios has an area of 76 square units and another has an area of 54 square units, what is the difference in area between them?

Answer: Marks: /3

Today's Marks: /7

Day Three Try these.

1. The souvenir shop sells candles in the shape of a wizard hat. How many surfaces there are on 7 of these candles?

Answer: | Marks: | /1

2. The Hollywood Scoops ice-cream parlour sells a delicious frozen dessert called the Prince of Egypt Special. Can you identify its 3-D shape? (Hint: It has 5 faces.)

Answer: | Marks: | /1

3. As well as rolls and sandwiches, the Starring Rolls Café sells a selection of tempting treats. Can you identify the 3-D shapes in the desserts shown?

 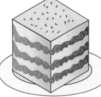  

Answer: | Marks: | /2

4. The studios were built using cube and cuboid shapes. Design your own studio based on the 3-D shapes that you have learned about.

Top tip: Make a model.

Answer: | Marks: | /3

Today's Marks: | /7

Day Four Try these.

(1) 8 l 250 ml of Slush Puppie drinks are sold one Saturday at the Hollywood Scoops ice-cream parlour. The following day, 9 l 740 ml of Slush Puppie drinks were sold. In litres and millilitres, how much was sold altogether that weekend?

Answer: | Marks: | /1

(2) The manager at the Starring Rolls Café drinks four 500 ml bottles of water each day. How much water does she drink daily?

Top tip:
Identify a pattern.

Answer: | Marks: | /2

(3) Last week, the Hollywood Scoops ice-cream parlour sold 100 litres of ice-cream. If 65 litres were sold on weekdays, how many were sold at the weekend?

Answer: | Marks: | /3

Today's Marks: | /6

Duties

Reader
Calculator
Checker
Reporter

Super Sleuth investigates

1. Can you identify any symmetry in the image?

2. Can you think of any maths questions based on the image?

30  Strategy: Working Backwards

Day One

Working backwards is a very useful problem-solving strategy. It helps us to solve maths stories that are missing a piece of information. We can find the missing piece of information by starting with the answer and working backwards, step by step. Here is an example:

Logan is thinking of a number. She adds 2 to it and gets 5. What was her starting number?

We can use inverse operations to help us as follows:

3 + 2 = 5   5 − 2 = 3   Answer: 3

Use the strategy of working backwards to answer the questions that follow. Share your solutions with one another and explain how you worked out the answers.

Try these.

1. Ely was in school for 6 hours today. If school finished at 3:30 pm, at what time did it start?

Answer: ⬚ Marks: ⬚ /1

2. Jayden's gran gave him money for his ninth birthday. He used the money to buy a football for €15 and a pair of football shorts for €25. He had €10 left over. How much money did his gran give him?

Answer: ⬚ Marks: ⬚ /2

3. There are beautiful tulips growing in Felicity's garden. Half of them are yellow, one-quarter of them are pink and the rest are red. If there are 5 red tulips, how many tulips are there altogether?

Answer: ⬚ Marks: ⬚ /3

Today's Marks: ⬚ /6

Day Two Try these.

Use the strategy of working backwards to solve each number story below.

Ⓒ LUE's

Duties

Reader

Calculator

Checker

Reporter

1 Hailey and 15 other pupils got on the school bus outside Hailey's house. At the next stop, a further 20 pupils got on the bus. When the bus arrived at school, all 60 pupils got off. How many pupils were already on the bus before it stopped at Hailey's house?

Answer: _____ Marks: ☐ /1

2 Cora made her own birthday party invitations and decorated them with a packet of stars. She used 17 stars on the invitations, a further 22 stars on the envelopes and had 12 stars left over. How many stars were in the packet to begin with?

Answer: _____ Marks: ☐ /1

3 Aubree and her sister Parker are playing snap. Parker has won 7 times and Aubree has won double that amount of times. If Aubree also played two games of snap with their brother beforehand, how many games has she played in total?

Answer: _____ Marks: ☐ /2

4 Scott bought a big bag of seedless grapes at the supermarket. He ate 50 g as he walked out of the supermarket and stopped to eat another 75 g in the car park. They were simply too tasty! By the time he arrived home, he had eaten another 75 g, but there was 300 g left in the bag. How much did the bag of grapes weigh to begin with?

Answer: _____ Marks: ☐ /3

Today's Marks: ☐ /7   125

Day Three Try these.

Use the strategy of working backwards to solve each number story below.

1 Harry went to the library to borrow some books. If he spent 25 minutes in the library and left at 7:45 pm, at what time did he enter the library?

Answer: | **Marks:** | /1

2 At Pizza Shack, Lucy paid for her order of a large cheese pizza costing €10.25, garlic bread costing €4.50 and ice-cream costing €6.00. The cashier gave her €9.25 in change. How much money had Lucy given the cashier?

Answer: | **Marks:** | /1

3 At the funfair, a number of children were queuing for the bumper-car ride. There were 8 bumper cars with 2 seats in each. When the ride began, the cars were full and there were 4 children still queuing. How many children were there in total?

Answer: | **Marks:** | /2

4 At the cinema, Leona's mum filled a bag of pick 'n' mix sweets. Leona then added 20 g of her favourite sweets to the bag before her mum went to the counter to pay. During the film, they ate 10 g of jelly beans, 20 g of chocolate-covered peanuts and 21 g of cola bottles between them. At the end of the film, there was 50 g of sweets left over. What was the weight of the bag before Leona added her favourite sweets?

pick n mix

Answer: | **Marks:** | /3

Today's Marks: | /7

Day Four Try these.

Use the strategy of working backwards to solve each number story below.

① Scarlett baked some buns for the school cake sale. 12 buns were sold. Scarlett gave 10 buns to the school secretary to take home. There were 8 buns left over. How many buns did Scarlett bake?

Answer: ⬚ Marks: ⬚ /1

② Alex's mum opened a full bottle of juice and poured a glass containing 100 ml for Alex and each of his 5 friends. If there was 400 ml left in the bottle, how much did it contain to begin with?

Answer: ⬚ Marks: ⬚ /1

③ Answer this question and then think of similar questions for your partner: I think of a number and multiply it by 2. The answer is 24. What was the number?

Answer: ⬚ Marks: ⬚ /2

④ Ann bought 2 school uniforms costing €60.50 each and a pair of shoes. If the total cost was €150, how much did the shoes cost?

Answer: ⬚ Marks: ⬚ /3

Today's Marks: ⬚ /7

Total Marks: ⬚ /27 | I would like to get better at ⬚

I'm happy that I know more about ⬚